HOUGHTON MIFFLIN

Georgia Science

HOUGHTON MIFFLIN

Printed in the U.S.A.
ISBN 13: 978-0-547-12513-8
ISBN 10: 0-547-12513-5

4 5 6 7 8 9 0877 15 14 13 12 11 10

Contents

WHAT DO YOU KNOW?

Tell what you know about how Earth's surface changes.

a. How Earth's surface is worn down:

_____

_____

_____

b. How Earth's surface is built up:

_____

_____

_____

Earth's Changing Surface

Contents

WHAT DO YOU WANT TO KNOW?

List something you want to know about each of these topics:

a. What makes up Earth's surface:

_____

_____

_____

b. How Earth's surface is worn down:

_____

_____

_____

c. How Earth's surface is built up:

_____

_____

_____

VOCABULARY

contour lines Lines on a topographical map that indicate areas with the same elevation, or height above sea level. *(noun)*

crust The thin, rocky outer layer of Earth that makes up the continents and the ocean floor. *(noun)*

topographical map Map that shows the shape of surface features and their elevations above sea level. *(noun)*

VOCABULARY SKILL: Context Clues

The word *crust* is used for many kinds of hard, outer parts. A pie has a crust, as does a loaf of bread. In the context of Earth science, *crust* refers to the hard, thin outer layer of Earth. Use the word *crust* in a sentence that helps explain the meaning of the word.

_____

_____

_____

1 What Makes Up Earth's Surface?

Earth's surface includes solid landforms and water. You can identify surface features by their location, shape, and elevation.

Earth's Solid Surface

Earth's rocky outer layer is called the **crust**. Different features, or parts, make up the surface of the crust. These features are found on the continents. Continents are huge masses of land on Earth's surface. Features found on the continents are often called landforms. Features of the crust are also found on the ocean floor.

Mountains are the tallest of Earth's landforms. Their steep slopes rise to tall peaks.

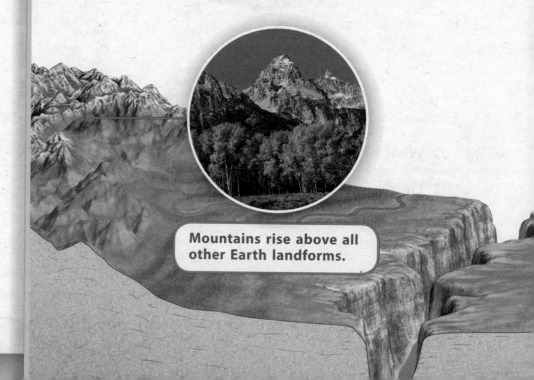

Mountains rise above all other Earth landforms.

  S5E1. Students will identify surface features of the Earth caused by constructive and destructive processes.

Hills are smaller than mountains. They do not rise as high as mountains. But their rounded tops still stand above the land around them.

Mountain valleys are long, narrow areas of low land between mountains or hills. Deep valleys with steep sides are called canyons.

Plateaus are high landforms with mostly flat surfaces. Plateaus are often found along the tops of canyons. Mesas are like plateaus, but much smaller.

Plains are broad and flat. In the middle of the United States are wide plains.

A river valley has a river flowing through it. The river usually flows through the center of the valley.

A flood plain is the floor of a river valley on either side of the river. Water covers a flood plain when a river rises above its banks.

River valleys are found in mountains, hills, and plains.

Plateaus are high, flat areas.

1. Earth's surface includes solid —————— and ——————.

2. Read the information on page 4. (Circle) three ways you can identify surface features.

3. Describe each of these landforms.
    a. mountain:
        ————————————————
        ————————————————
    b. plateau:
        ————————————————
        ————————————————
    c. flood plain:
        ————————————————
        ————————————————

5

4. Study the circle graph on page 6. Tell how much of earth's surface is covered by each material.

a. land: _____

b. fresh water: _____

c. salt water: _____

5. Circle the word on the graph that shows where the largest portion of fresh water is located.

A Watery Planet

Earth is the only planet we know of with a lot of water. Most of that water is found in the oceans. An ocean is a huge body of salt water. All of Earth's oceans are connected. They form one great world ocean. The world ocean surrounds the continents.

Some of Earth's water is on the continents. Most of the water on the continents, called inland water, is not salty. Water with little salt is called fresh water. Lakes and rivers are the main Earth features that hold or carry fresh water. Streams and ponds also hold fresh water. Most fresh water is found underground or in glaciers or ice sheets near Earth's poles.

Plants, humans, and other animals all need fresh water. Yet only a small part of Earth's water is fresh water. For these reasons, fresh water is a very important resource.

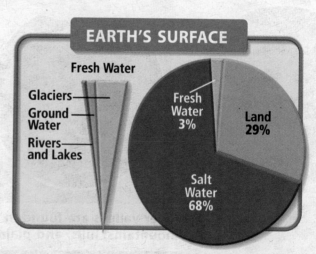

EARTH'S SURFACE

Fresh Water

Glaciers

Ground Water

Rivers and Lakes

Fresh Water 3%

Land 29%

Salt Water 68%

This graph shows how much of Earth's surface is covered by land, salt water, and fresh water.

Coastal Features

Different landforms are found near water. A coastal plain is a wide, flat area near an ocean. Where dry land meets the ocean is called the shore. Beaches and marshlands form there. Beaches are flat landforms along an ocean or large lake. Marshlands are areas of shallow water where water plants grow.

Beaches can be sandy or rocky. Beaches can be small or very long. Some beaches have sand dunes. Sand dunes are mounds or ridges of sand that the wind often forms along coastlines.

Sometimes shores do not have beaches. Instead, the coastline is rocky. Steep cliffs and mountains rise along the water's edge. Ocean waves pound against rocky coastlines. The waves make interesting features. These features include beaches, sea caves, sea cliffs, and sea arches.

Coastal plains are low areas that slope gently from the land toward the shore.

Beaches may be rocky, pebbly, or sandy. Some beaches are a mix of all three.

Circle the correct answer.

6. Which of these surface features can be formed by ocean waves?

   A. sea caves

   B. mountains

   C. volcanoes

   D. ponds

S5E1

7. Compare a marsh with a beach.

	Marsh	Beach
Where found		
Description		

8. Place an X on the diagram that shows where a river enters the ocean.

9. List the three parts of the continental margin.

   a. _____

   b. _____

   c. _____

Ocean Floor Features

A feature called the continental margin starts at the water's edge. It stretches hundreds of miles to the deep ocean floor. The continental margin is made up of three parts. These parts are the continental shelf, the continental slope, and the continental rise.

The continental shelf forms the edges of a continent. A shelf usually slopes gently down from sea level to a depth of less than 200 m (660 ft). It can be from 80 km (48 mi) to more than 1,000 km (600 mi) wide.

Farther from the shelf is the continental slope. The continental slope drops sharply. It forms the sides of the continents. At the bottom of the slope is the continental rise.

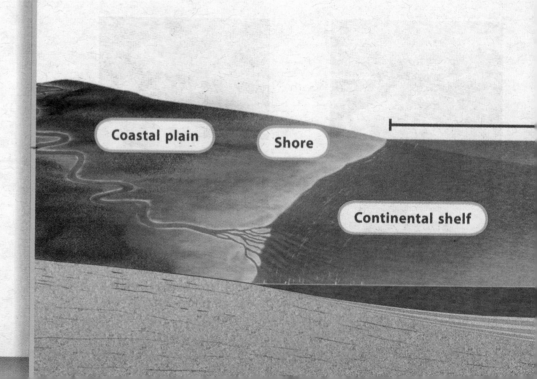

Coastal plain

Shore

Continental shelf

The ocean floor has many features. Some are like those on dry land. Underwater canyons slice through the continental shelf. Such canyons are called submarine canyons.

Mountains and plains are under water, too. Seamounts are huge, steep-sided mountains rising from the ocean floor. Some seamounts have flat tops. These are called guyots (GEE ohs).

Seamounts are found mainly on the deep ocean floor. This huge area is known as the abyssal plain.

Seamounts may rise thousands of meters above the ocean floor.

Continental margin

Continental slope

Continental rise

10. Compare and contrast guyots and submarine canyons.

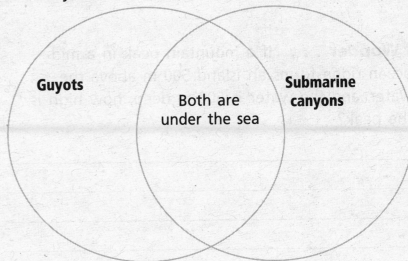

Guyots

Both are under the sea

Submarine canyons

11. (Circle) the mid-ocean ridge in the diagram on page 10.

I Wonder . . . If a mountain peak in a mid-ocean ridge forms an island 500 m above the water, and the water is 600 m deep, how high is the peak?

_____

_____

_____

_____

Mid-Ocean Features

Many features of the ocean floor are found in the ocean basin. The ocean basin is the area far from the continental margin.

In the ocean basin, deep canyons called trenches cut into the ocean floor. Underwater mountain chains called mid-ocean ridges run more than 56,000 km (33,600 mi) through the world ocean. Most mountains in the mid-ocean ridges reach more than 1,500 m (4,950 ft) high. Some peaks stick out of the water as islands.

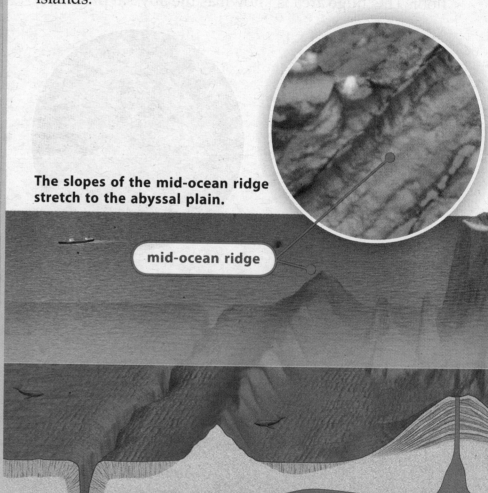

The slopes of the mid-ocean ridge stretch to the abyssal plain.

mid-ocean ridge

Mapping Surface Features

A **topographic map** is a map that shows the shape of surface features and their elevations. Elevation is the height of a landform above sea level. **Contour lines** connect points on the map that have the same elevation. By studying contour lines, you can learn the shape and steepness of the land.

This topographic map shows Mount Rainier in Washington State. The numbers on the contour lines show elevation in feet. The space of the lines shows how steeply the land slopes.

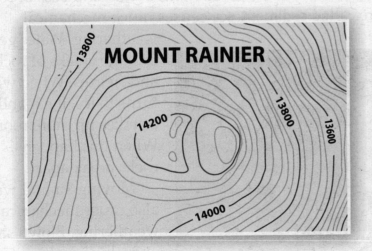

MOUNT RAINIER

13800
14200
13800
13600
14000

Summary   Earth's surface includes water and solid landforms. You can identify surface features by their location, shape, and elevation.

What do the lines on the topographical map on page 11 tell you?

_____

_____

_____

▶ **Main Idea and Details**   Name six of Earth's landforms.

Main Idea
Earth has different landforms.

MAIN IDEA AND DETAILS

Name six of Earth's landforms.

Lesson Preview

VOCABULARY

erosion Destructive force in which pieces of rock are moved by water, wind, or moving ice. *(noun)*

sediment Small pieces of rock. *(noun)*

weathering Destructive force that breaks down rocks into smaller pieces. *(noun)*

VOCABULARY SKILL: Use Pictures

Pictures help you know the meaning of a word. Look at the pictures on these pages. What do you know about *weathering* from these pictures?

_____

_____

_____

 S5E1b. Identify and find samples of surface features caused by destructive processes.

12

2 How Is Earth's Surface Worn Down?

Weathering and erosion are forces that wear down Earth's surface. Such forces are called destructive forces because they break things down.

Weathering

Earth's crust is made mostly of rock. The rocks are broken into pieces by weathering. **Weathering** is a destructive force. There are two types of weathering: mechanical and chemical.

Mechanical weathering is the breaking of larger rocks into smaller pieces. These smaller pieces of rock are called **sediment**. Ice causes much mechanical weathering. Water gets into the cracks of rocks and freezes. When water turns to ice, it expands, or takes up more room. When this happens, rocks break apart.

Moving air and water also cause mechanical weathering. Blown sand or rushing water hits rocks, and the rocks get weaker. Over time, they crack or crumble.

Plants can grow through cracks and break apart rocks.

Mechanical weathering breaks rocks, but it does not change the kind of rock. In chemical weathering, rocks change into other materials.

Water causes most chemical weathering. Water can dissolve some rocks, or break them down into parts that become part of the water.

Water trickling through the ground can dissolve some rocks far under the surface. Caves are hollow spaces under the ground that are formed by weathering. Most caves are made from limestone. Weak acid dissolves limestone easily. Water seeps into the ground and dissolves some rock.

Over time, holes form in the rock. The holes grow, forming passages, chambers, and pits. Slowly they become caves.

Cave Formation

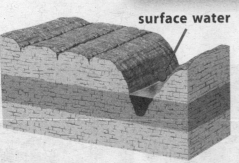

surface water

Water and weak acids seep into the ground.

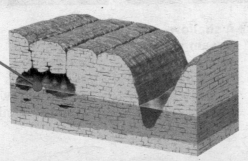

cave

Over time, holes are formed. Slowly, the holes grow into caves.

1. List one example of each kind of weathering.
   a. mechanical weathering:

   _____
   _____
   _____

   b. chemical weathering:

   _____
   _____
   _____

2. Draw a diagram that shows how a cave forms over time.

3. The carrying away of sediments by moving water, wind, or moving ice is called

_____.

GPS CRCT Prep

Circle the correct answer.

4. A river cutting a V-shaped valley is an example of

   A. a sinkhole.

   B. a landslide.

   C. weathering and erosion.

   D. a constructive process.

S5E1b

Erosion

The carrying away of sediments by moving water, wind, or moving ice is called **erosion**.

Water moving down a river causes much erosion. The river begins as a shallow stream, often high up in the mountains. The water flows downhill and wears away the ground. It dissolves some rocks and picks up sediments from the bottom of the stream. Over time, the stream becomes wider and deeper.

Usually a stream joins other streams to become a river. Now there is more water and tumbling rocks. These forces cause more erosion in the river. This erosion may carve out a steeper or wider river valley. Sometimes, fast cutting of the valley floor in the upper part of a river can form a canyon.

River Valley Formation

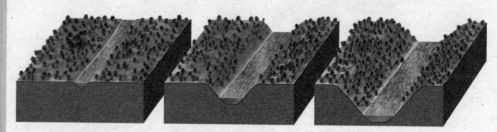

❶ A shallow stream slowly wears away the ground.

❷ The stream grows into a river. The river carries sediment away from its banks.

❸ In time, the river forms a river valley.

14

Frozen water also wears down and shapes Earth's surface features. Thousands of years ago, huge sheets of ice called glaciers helped to shape the rolling plains in the northern United States. They also carved out the Great Lakes.

Glaciers also can push huge amounts of sediments along the bottoms and sides of the ice. The sediments grind against the surface below. This grinding carves out hollows in the land.

Ocean waves and flowing water also wear down Earth's surface. Crashing waves break down rock along the coast. Waves drag the sediments back and forth, slowing turning them into sand. Water and sediments pound at narrow sections of land that jut into the water. Such erosion cuts out features called sea caves and sea arches.

A sea arch forms when water and sediment carve away rocky land that juts into the water.

I Wonder . . . How could you tell whether a glacier had once moved across a region?

_____

_____

_____

_____

5. Compare and contrast sinkholes and landslides.

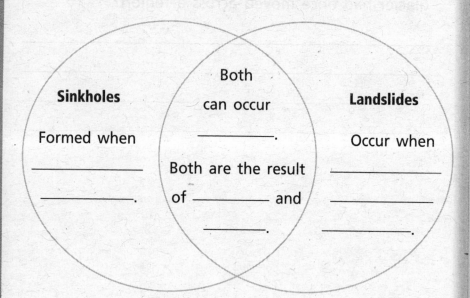

Sinkholes

Formed when

_____

_____.

Both

can occur

_____.

Both are the result

of _____ and

_____.

Landslides

Occur when

_____

_____

_____.

Slow and Fast Changes

Erosion keeps changing the landscape. In general, destructive forces act very slowly. However, sometimes such changes happen much faster.

Caves can take thousands of years to form. However, after a cave has formed, the rock above the cave often has little support. At some point, the rock above the cave may sink or fall into the hole made by the cave. This is called a sinkhole.

Sinkholes can form very suddenly. One large sinkhole formed in a single day in Winter Park, Florida. The city sealed it and made a lake.

A sinkhole forms when weathered rock sinks into a hole. This sinkhole formed in Florida.

An alluvial fan forms when a river slows suddenly and its sediment is dropped. A delta forms in the same way.

Deposition helps form a number of surface features. Several of these features form as part of river systems. A river usually begins at a high point on Earth's surface. At first the water flows quickly downhill and carries sediment with it. At the mouth, or end of the river, the water usually empties into a large body of water, such as a lake or ocean.

Near the mouth, the land is flatter. Water flows more slowly over flat land. The sediment drops out of the water. A delta is a low plain that forms where a river enters an ocean.

Sometimes a river rushes down a steep slope, then slows over a flat plain. There, a fan-shaped deposit called an alluvial fan forms.

1. Fill in the blanks to explain how a delta forms.

Water flows quickly ——————— and carries ——————— with it.

At the mouth of the river, water empties into a larger body of water, such as a ——————— or an ———————.

At the mouth of the river, water slows down and flows more slowly over ——————— land.

The ——————— drops out of the water to form a ———————.

2. What are two ways that surface features can result from magma pushing up Earth's crust?

a. _____

_____

_____

b. _____

_____

_____

CPS · CRCT Prep

Circle the correct answer.

3. **Magma flowing out of Earth's crust formed which of the following features?**

   A. the Himalayas

   B. the Mississippi River delta

   C. the islands off the coast of Georgia

   D. the islands of Hawaii

`S5E1a`

Pushing Up Earth's Surface

Earth's features can be pushed up from below as well as built up from above. Not far below Earth's surface, it is very hot. In some places, it is hot enough to melt rock!

Melted rock below Earth's surface is called magma. Magma is formed in a layer of Earth just below the crust. Pressure below the surface can cause magma to push up on Earth's crust. This pushing forms round, dome-shaped mountains.

In some places, magma can work its way up through the crust and flow out onto Earth's surface. Magma at Earth's surface is called lava. As lava flows, it cools and hardens into rock.

Building Islands

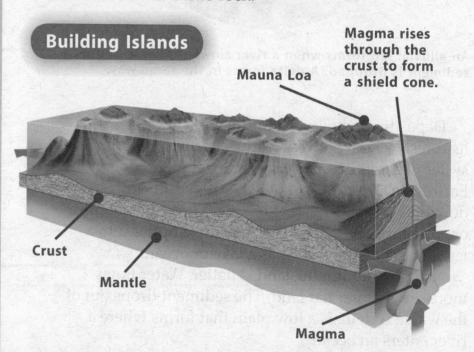

Magma rises through the crust to form a shield cone.

Mauna Loa

Crust

Mantle

Magma

The Hawaiian Islands are a group of shield cones. They rise from the floor of the Pacific Ocean to well above its surface.

This photo of Hawaii was taken from the International Space Station. Mauna Loa rises in the center of the island.

In other places, enough lava will build up to form a huge deposit with gently sloping sides. Such deposits are called shield cones. Shield cones often form on the ocean floor. If they rise above the water, they form islands. The Hawaiian Islands are the tops of several giant shield cones. The base of Mauna Loa, the largest of these cones, is about 4,500 m (15,000 ft) below the surface of the Pacific Ocean. Its peak rises over 4,100 m (14,000 ft) above the ocean's surface.

4. Huge deposits of lava with gently sloping sides are called ———————— ————————.

5. Determine the height of Mauna Loa, the largest shield cone mountain on the Hawaiian Islands.

   Below the ocean surface: ————————

   Above the ocean surface: ————————

   Total height: ————————

6. What process formed the Himalayas?

_____

_____

I Wonder . . . Some of Earth's features are made of the remains of living things. How were the chalk cliffs of Dover formed?

_____

_____

_____

_____

Building Mountains

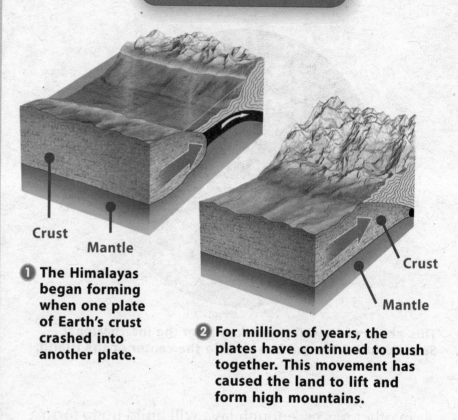

Crust

Mantle

① The Himalayas began forming when one plate of Earth's crust crashed into another plate.

Crust

Mantle

② For millions of years, the plates have continued to push together. This movement has caused the land to lift and form high mountains.

A different constructive force is the movement of huge pieces of Earth's crust. These moving pieces of crust can crash into each other and cause the crust to fold. When this happens, the crust rises to form high mountains. The Himalaya Mountains began forming in this way about 65 million years ago.

Other features of Earth are made from the remains of living things. For example, the chalk cliffs of Dover, England, are made up of shells of tiny sea animals. These shells were deposited on the sea floor millions of years ago. When forces below the crust raised the sea floor, the chalk deposits became chalk cliffs.

Coral reefs are another type of Earth feature made from the remains of living things. In shallow tropical waters, tiny animals called corals gather in colonies. As corals die, their skeletons build up into a bumpy ridge called a reef.

In some Pacific Ocean waters, reefs are built around islands. Sometimes an island will sink, but the coral continues to grow. The reef forms a ring-shaped island called an atoll.

Atolls are ring-shaped islands formed from coral reefs.

7. Compare and contrast chalk cliffs and coral reefs.

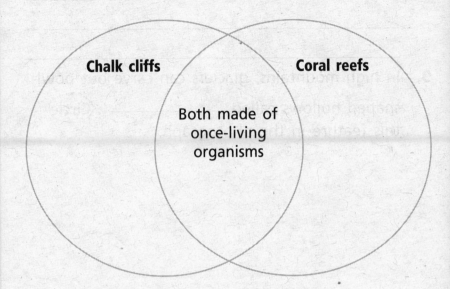

Chalk cliffs   **Coral reefs**

Both made of once-living organisms

8. How do glaciers move materials?

_____

_____

_____

9. In high mountains, glaciers can carve out bowl-shaped hollows called _____. (Circle) this feature in the photograph.

Glacial Deposits

Thousands of years ago, snow fell year-round over large areas of Asia, Europe, and North America. Over time, the weight of snow from the top added pressure below. Slowly, the snow turned to ice. Glaciers were formed.

The ice in some of these glaciers was almost 1,000 m thick. The weight of the ice became so great that it pushed and dented the land.

These moving masses of ice were great forces of erosion. Huge amounts of soil and rock were pushed ahead of the ice and carried along in the glacier's bottom layers.

After thousands of years, the ice began to melt. When the ice melted, it left the land changed.

In high mountains, glaciers can carve out bowl-shaped hollows called cirques.

Cirque

The rocky sediment deposited by a glacier is known as till. Till may be fine soil, sand, gravel, boulders, or sharp rocks. Some till is picked up as a glacier scrapes Earth's surface. The glacier drags till along its icy base.

A glacier also deposits till at its front. Such deposits are called moraines. Long Island, New York, is a moraine left when a huge ice sheet melted.

Streams flow through tunnels in melting glaciers. The streams deposit sand and gravel in ridges. These winding ridges are called eskers.

Eskers form from streams that flow along the bottoms of melting glaciers.

CAUSE AND EFFECT

How do glaciers deposit sediment?

Summary   Forces such as deposition and volcanic activity build up Earth's surface features.

List two ways glaciers build up the land.

a. _____

b. _____

▶ **Cause and Effect**   How do glaciers deposit sediment?

Cause		Effect
Glaciers build up sediments when they move.	→	

25

Visit www.eduplace.com to play puzzles and word games.

Draw a picture illustrating contour lines.

Write a sentence that includes two words from this page.

_____

_____

_____

_____

Glossary

contour lines (KAHN tur lynz), lines on a topographic map that indicate areas with the same elevation, or height above sea level.

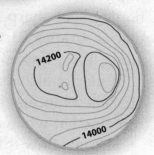

crust (kruhst), the thin, rocky outer layer of Earth that makes up the continents and the ocean floor.

deposition (dehp uh ZIHSH uhn), [1] constructive force in which sediments that have been moved from one place are dropped or released in another place, or [2] change of state from a gas to a solid.

erosion (ih ROH zhuhn), destructive force in which pieces of rock are moved by water, wind, or moving ice.

sediment (SEHD uh muhnt), small pieces of rock

topographic map (tah pah GRAF ihk map), map that shows the shape of surface features and their elevations above sea level

weathering (WEHTH uhr ihng), destructive force that breaks down rocks into smaller pieces

Responding

Think About What You Have Read

❶ Erosion and weathering are examples of _____

   A. constructive forces.

   B. destructive forces.

   C. surface features.

   D. land buildup.

Comprehension

S5E1b

❷ Name and tell about the three parts of the continental margin.

❸ Describe how a cave is formed.

❹ How were the Himalaya Mountains formed?

Critical Thinking

❺ What features on the ocean floor are like features on Earth's surface?

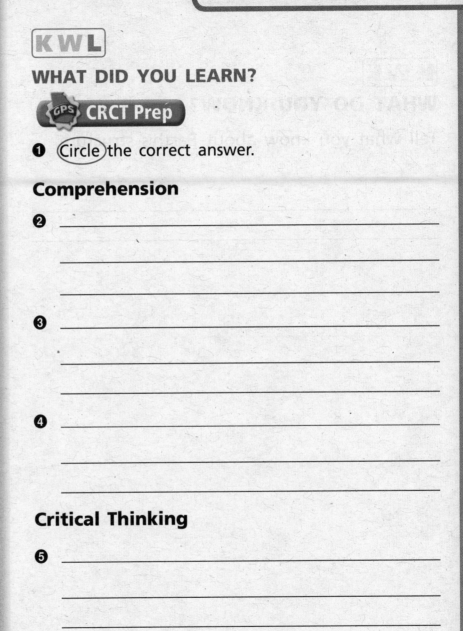

Chapter Review

KWL

WHAT DID YOU LEARN?

GPS CRCT Prep

❶ (Circle) the correct answer.

Comprehension

❷ _____

_____

_____

❸ _____

_____

❹ _____

_____

_____

Critical Thinking

❺ _____

_____

_____

WHAT DO YOU KNOW?

Tell what you know about Earth's structure.

_____

_____

_____

Earth's Structure

Contents

 K W L

WHAT DO YOU WANT TO KNOW?

Skim the pictures and headings in this chapter. List one thing you want to find out about each of these topics

a. Earth's structure:

_____

_____

_____

b. Earthquakes and volcanoes:

_____

_____

_____

c. How mountains are formed:

_____

_____

_____

VOCABULARY

core Earth's innermost structure. *(noun)*

crust The thin, rocky, outer layer of Earth that makes up the continents and the ocean floor. *(noun)*

lithosphere Shell formed from Earth's solid upper mantle and crust. *(noun)*

mantle Thick layer of Earth's structure just below Earth's crust. *(noun)*

plate tectonics Theory that giant plates of crust are moving slowly across Earth's surface. *(noun)*

VOCABULARY SKILL: Word Origins

The word *lithosphere* is made up of two words: *litho*, which is a Greek word meaning "rock" or "stone," and *sphere*, which means "a round body." Given these definitions, what might the word *lithosphere* mean?

_____

How does that definition relate to the definition given above?

_____

_____

 S5E1a. Identify surface features caused by constructive processes.
S5E1b. Identify and find examples of surface features caused by destructive processes.

30

1 What Is Earth's Structure?

Earth has four layers. Its outer layer is made up of moving parts called plates.

Hot Inside

In many parts of the world, columns of steaming hot water shoot up from Earth's surface. These boiling fountains are known as geysers. Geysers form in places where water drains down a deep channel, or thin tunnel, in Earth's surface. At the bottom of the channel, hot rocks heat the water until steam forms. The steam pushes boiling water up to the surface. Finally, the built-up pressure forces the rest of the water to erupt, or burst out. The existence of geysers tells us that Earth is very hot inside.

Geysers are boiling fountains of water. The water in geysers is heated by hot rocks under Earth's surface.

People have studied temperatures, or measures of heat, inside mines and holes drilled in Earth's crust. In this way, they have learned that the temperature rises about 2 to 3°C for every 0.1 km (300 ft) below the surface.

However, they cannot drill very deep into Earth. But they can study geysers and volcanoes to learn about the temperature inside Earth. They also test rocks under high pressure and temperature.

People also can learn about the inside of Earth by studying seismic waves. Seismic waves are vibrations, or back-and-forth movements, that travel through Earth during earthquakes. Seismic waves change as they travel deeper into Earth. They also change as they move through different kinds of materials at different temperatures.

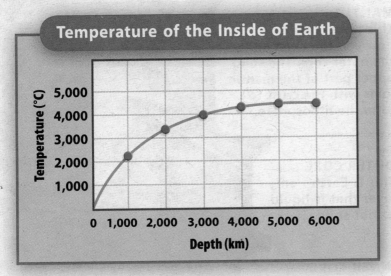

Earth's temperature rises about 25°C per km in the crust. It rises less from the upper mantle to the center.

1. What is the next step in the formation of a geyser?

Hot rocks at the bottom of a deep channel heat water until steam forms.

2. Look at the graph. Place an X on the temperature that a depth of 6,000 kilometers would register.

3. Which of Earth's layers is made up of solid metals?

_____

4. Draw a diagram of Earth's layers. Label each layer.

I Wonder . . . Which of Earth's layers has the hottest temperatures? Why?

_____

_____

_____

Earth's Layers

Earth is made up of layers. Most of these layers are made up of solid or partly melted rock. The layers closest to the middle of Earth are mostly a mixture of metals.

Each layer has a different thickness. The outer layer, or **crust**, is much thinner than the other layers. The crust is nearly all solid rock.

Under the continents the average thickness of the crust is about 40 km (24 mi). Under mountains it may be as much as 70 km (42 mi) thick. The crust is thinner under the oceans. The ocean floor crust has a thickness of about 7 km (4 mi).

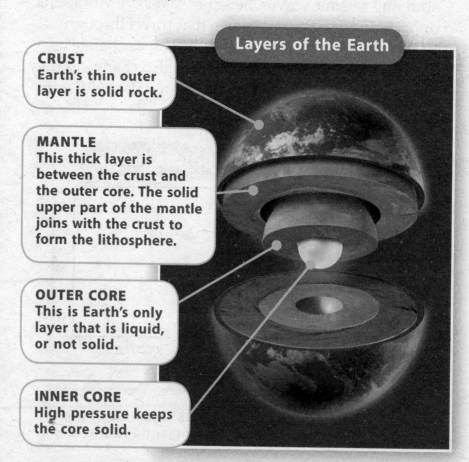

Layers of the Earth

CRUST
Earth's thin outer layer is solid rock.

MANTLE
This thick layer is between the crust and the outer core. The solid upper part of the mantle joins with the crust to form the lithosphere.

OUTER CORE
This is Earth's only layer that is liquid, or not solid.

INNER CORE
High pressure keeps the core solid.

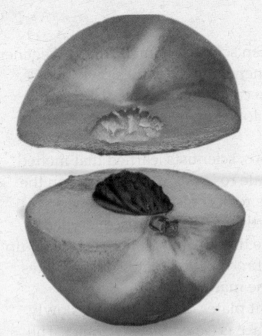

A peach can be used as a model of Earth. The peach pit stands for the core.

The layer just below Earth's crust is the **mantle**. The mantle is about 2,900 km (1,800 mi) thick. It is the thickest layer. The solid upper part of the mantle joins with the crust to form the **lithosphere**.

Below the lithosphere, much of the rock in the mantle is partly melted. This material can flow very slowly. The hard lithosphere can be thought of as "floating" on the lower mantle.

At the center of Earth is the **core**. The core is divided into two layers—the outer core and the inner core. The outer core is about 2,200 km (1,400 mi) thick. It is the only layer that is all liquid.

The inner core is about 1,200 km (720 mi) thick. It is even hotter than the outer core. Both the outer core and the inner core are probably made up of very hot iron and nickel. High pressure deep inside Earth keeps the metals from melting.

5. Which layer of Earth is liquid? Explain your answer.

_____

_____

_____

6. In what ways would an apple be useful as a model of Earth?

_____

_____

_____

33

7. Fill in the blanks to describe the development of plate tectonics theory.

a. Alfred _____ said that the continents move very slowly across _____ surface.

b. He called his idea the theory of _____ _____ .

c. That theory led to the discovery of _____ _____ , which explains that huge plates in the _____ are able to move very slowly across Earth's surface.

8. How many kilometers will an average plate have moved during the lifetime of an 80-year-old person?

80 years × _____ per year = _____ cm = _____ km

Moving Plates

In 1915 a German scientist named Alfred Wegener said that the continents moved very slowly across Earth's surface. He called his idea the theory of continental drift. However, he could not explain it completely.

Then in the 1950s, scientists learned that melted rock from the mantle rose to Earth's surface on the ocean floor. As this rock cooled and hardened, it became part of Earth's crust. This discovery led scientists to believe that the lithosphere is broken up into giant pieces of rock called plates. These plates "float" on top of the mantle.

The idea of giant plates of rock moving slowly across Earth's surface is called **plate tectonics**. The plates move very slowly. Their average speed is about 10 cm (4 in.) a year. However, over millions of years, plates can move thousands of kilometers.

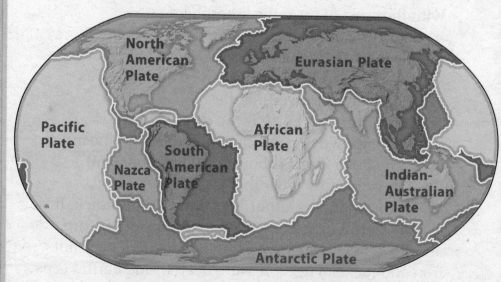

This map shows Earth's major plates.

Kinds of Plate Boundaries

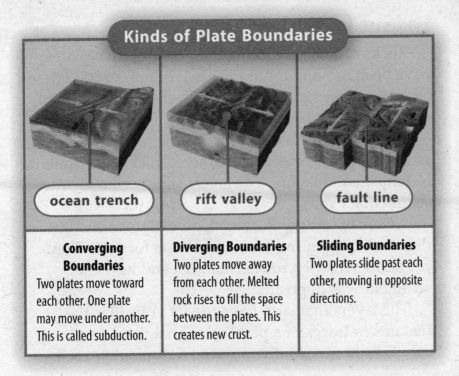

ocean trench	rift valley	fault line
Converging Boundaries Two plates move toward each other. One plate may move under another. This is called subduction.	**Diverging Boundaries** Two plates move away from each other. Melted rock rises to fill the space between the plates. This creates new crust.	**Sliding Boundaries** Two plates slide past each other, moving in opposite directions.

The places where one plate meets another plate are called plate boundaries. Different things happen at plate boundaries. There are three types of boundaries.

At converging boundaries, two plates converge, or move toward each other. Sooner or later, they crash into each other. One plate may ride up over the other. The upper plate pushes the edge of the lower plate under the surface. This is called subduction.

At diverging boundaries, two plates move away, or diverge, from each other. Melted rock rises up between the plates and forms new crust. This generally happens in the middle of the ocean floor, so it is called sea-floor spreading.

In some places, plates slide past each other. These places are known as sliding boundaries.

9. List the three kinds of plate boundaries.

a. _____

b. _____

c. _____

 CRCT Prep

Circle the correct answer.

10. **When two plates move away from each other, the boundary is**

A. pushing.

B. sliding.

C. converging.

D. diverging.

S5E1a

11. List two clues about geological changes that layers of sedimentary rocks may contain.

a. _____

b. _____

12. Fill in the blanks to describe fossils.

a. A _____ is the remains or traces of a _____ or an _____ that lived long ago.

b. Fossils are usually found in _____ rock.

Evidence for Moving Plates

Rocks at Earth's surface show that Earth's plates have been moving for at least two billion years. These rocks have been eroded and deposited, or laid down, since Earth first took shape.

All rock at Earth's surface is broken down by weathering and erosion. Weathered rock, or sediment, is deposited in layers. The layers slowly change into sedimentary rock.

Layers of sedimentary rock give hints to changes that were happening when the layers formed. They can show what the rock is made of and how the sediment was deposited.

The layers may also have fossils. A **fossil** is the remains or traces of a plant or animal that lived long ago. Fossils are usually found in sedimentary rock.

A fossil of a tropical fern like this one was found in a snowy area. Ferns grow best in hot, wet places. Since this fossil formed, the region is believed to have moved 3,200 km (2,000 mi) on part of a continental plate.

By studying fossils in rock layers, scientists can get an idea of how plates moved in Earth's past. For example, fossils of similar kinds of plants and animals have been found along the edges of different continents. Scientists believe that the fossils come from a time when those continents were joined. Over millions of years, the continents drifted apart and the fossils were moved to new places.

Some fossils seem to be very far from where they formed. For example, fossils of fish have been found near the tops of mountains. Scientists believe that these fossils were carried there by plate movements.

TEXT STRUCTURE

Describe three ways in which Earth's plates move at their boundaries.

Summary Earth has a layered structure. Its outer layer is made up of moving plates.

How do fossils provide evidence for moving plates?

_____

_____

_____

▶ **Text Structure** Describe three ways in which Earth's plates move at their boundaries.

1) _____ 2) _____ 3) _____

37

VOCABULARY

earthquake Violent shaking of Earth's crust as built-up energy is released. *(noun)*

epicenter Point on Earth's surface directly above the focus of an earthquake. *(noun)*

fault Crack in Earth's surface along which movement takes place. *(noun)*

focus Point underground where the faulting in an earthquake occurs. *(noun)*

magma Melted rock below Earth's surface; called lava at the surface. *(noun)*

seismic waves Waves of energy sent through Earth's crust when parts of the crust move suddenly. *(noun)*

VOCABULARY SKILL: Word Parts

Find the two smaller words in *earthquake*. Say the words together. Write the two smaller words in this compound word.

———————— + ————————

S5E1b. Identify and find samples of surface features caused by destructive processes. (Earthquake, Volcano)

2 What Are Earthquakes and Volcanoes?

Earthquakes and volcanoes change Earth's surface, usually at plate boundaries.

At the Faults

Most major changes to Earth's surface happen at or near plate boundaries. At these boundaries there are faults. **Faults** are cracks in Earth's crust where movement takes place.

Along a fault, rocks often bend and fold. Sometimes they lock together and get stuck. The plates strain against each other. Over many years, stress builds up on the rocks. Finally the rocks break. The plates shudder and jolt into a new position. This sudden movement causes Earth's crust to shake. As the crust shakes, it sends out shock waves of energy known as **seismic waves**. A seismograph is an instrument used to measure the strength of seismic waves.

Different Kinds of Faults

Fault at Diverging Boundary

As pieces of the crust move apart, rocks are stretched until they snap. This causes one block to move down along a sloping crack.

The movement of rocks along a fault is called faulting. During faulting, the rocks crack to split into blocks. The blocks continue to move.

There are three main types of faults. Each fault is caused by a different type of force applied in the area that is moving.

At diverging boundaries, where plates are moving apart, the force stretches rock. The rock breaks, and one block moves down along a sloping crack.

Other faults happen at converging boundaries, where plates move toward each other. Here, the force squeezes rock. When the rock breaks, one block moves up along a sloping crack. At the same time, the other block moves down. Often this happens in places of subduction, where one plate plunges below the other.

The third type of fault happens in places where blocks move sideways past each other. These faults are common at sliding boundaries.

Fault at Converging Boundary	Fault at Sliding Boundary
Rocks are pressed together. This causes one block to move up along a sloping crack as the other moves down.	Rocks move sideways past each other in opposite directions. They grind against each other. Pressure builds up along the fault until the rocks break.

1. What does a seismograph register?

_____

_____

2. Identify each kind of fault shown and tell how the rocks move.

_____   _____   _____

_____   _____   _____

_____   _____   _____

_____   _____   _____

3. What causes an earthquake?

_____

_____

4. Draw a picture that shows the focus, waves, and epicenter of an earthquake. Label each part of your drawing.

Earthquakes

An **earthquake** is a violent shaking of Earth's crust. An earthquake is caused by the release of built-up energy along a fault. The energy released depends on how much rock breaks and how far the blocks of rock move.

The surface effects, or intensity, of an earthquake are different from place to place. Intensity is measured by what can be seen and felt on the surface.

What people see and feel often depends on how far they are from the earthquake's focus. The **focus** of an earthquake is the point right under the fault. Most focus points are less than 72 km (45 mi) below Earth's surface.

The point on the surface right above the focus is an earthquake's **epicenter**. Here the intensity is the strongest because the seismic waves at the focus of an earthquake are the strongest.

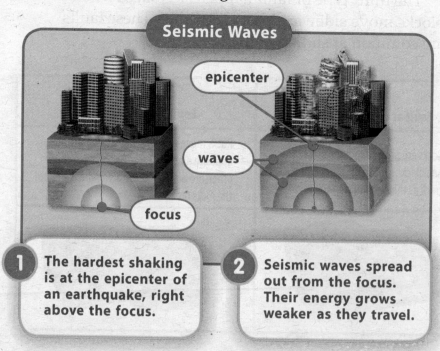

Seismic Waves

epicenter

waves

focus

1 The hardest shaking is at the epicenter of an earthquake, right above the focus.

2 Seismic waves spread out from the focus. Their energy grows weaker as they travel.

There are two main kinds of seismic waves—body waves and surface waves. Body waves move through the inside of Earth. They can pass through hard rock and liquid. Surface waves move along Earth's surface.

There are two kinds of body waves, P waves and S waves. When P waves reach the surface, they cause rock to move back and forth. When S waves reach the surface, they cause rock to move up and down.

Surface waves, or L waves, travel more slowly than body waves. They also do not travel too far from the epicenter of an earthquake. However, surface waves cause the most damage, because they make the ground swell and roll like ocean waves.

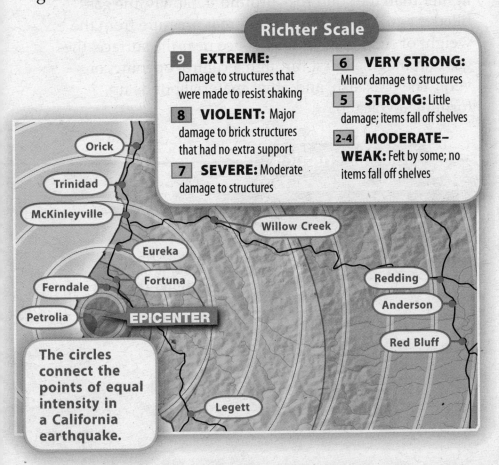

Richter Scale

9 EXTREME: Damage to structures that were made to resist shaking

8 VIOLENT: Major damage to brick structures that had no extra support

7 SEVERE: Moderate damage to structures

6 VERY STRONG: Minor damage to structures

5 STRONG: Little damage; items fall off shelves

2-4 MODERATE–WEAK: Felt by some; no items fall off shelves

Orick
Trinidad
McKinleyville
Willow Creek
Eureka
Fortuna
Redding
Anderson
Ferndale
Petrolia EPICENTER
Red Bluff
Legett

The circles connect the points of equal intensity in a California earthquake.

5. An earthquake measures 7.7 on the Richter scale. Would you expect that the blocks of rock at the earthquake's focus shifted a little or a lot? Explain.

_____

_____

6. Match the kind of seismic wave with the drawing that illustrates the way the wave causes rocks to move when it reaches the surface.

P waves

S waves

L waves

7. Tell the series of events that lead to the eruption of a volcano.

a. _____

_____

_____

b. _____

_____

_____

c. _____

_____

_____

d. _____

_____

_____

Volcanoes

A volcano is an opening in Earth's surface through which melted rock, hot gases, rock pieces, and ash burst forth, or erupt. When a volcano erupts, red-hot melted rock, poisonous gas, thick gray ash, and scorched rock pour or shoot out.

Volcanoes come from the inside of Earth. Most volcanoes start 37 to 100 miles below the surface. There, it is so hot that rock melts. Melted rock below Earth's surface is called **magma**.

When rock melts, it lets out gases. These gases mix with the magma. The added gas makes the magma lighter than the solid rock around it. Slowly, the gas-filled magma rises. It is under great pressure from the weight of surrounding rock. Once near the surface, the gas and magma burst through a central opening, or vent. The rock, ash, and other material builds up, forming a volcano.

Volcanic Eruption

1 Hot, gas-filled magma rises. As it does so, it melts rock along the way. Near the surface, it forms a magma-filled space called a chamber.

Three main kinds of material come out of volcanoes during an eruption. Most of the material is lava. Lava is the name for magma after it reaches the surface. Lava may be thin and flow fast. Or it may be thick and flow slowly. Flowing lava may be hotter than 1,100°C (2,000°F). As lava cools, it gets hard. It forms into different shapes.

Rock pieces may form when gas in sticky magma cannot escape. Pressure builds up until the gas blasts the magma apart. The pieces erupt into dust, ash, and large chunks called bombs. The largest bombs can be more that 1 m (3 ft) wide and weigh 100 tons!

Gases also escape when a volcano erupts. Gases from volcanoes are mostly steam. But they often have harmful chemicals in them. These gases mix with ash to form a deadly black smoke.

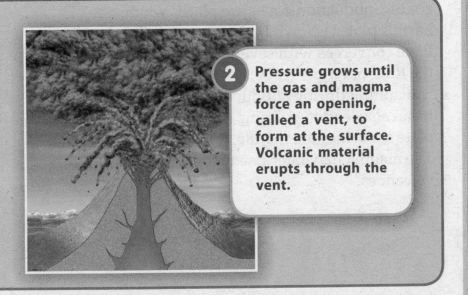

2 Pressure grows until the gas and magma force an opening, called a vent, to form at the surface. Volcanic material erupts through the vent.

I Wonder . . . If a volcano erupted on a windy day, how might the direction of the wind affect the decision about which areas people must leave, or evacuate?

_____

_____

_____

_____

_____

Circle the correct answer.

8. Where could you most likely observe a volcano?

A. northern Georgia

B. the rim of the Pacific Ocean

C. Florida

D. the Himalayas

S5E1b

There are many volcanoes and earthquakes along the edge of the Pacific Ocean. This explains why this area is called the Ring of Fire.

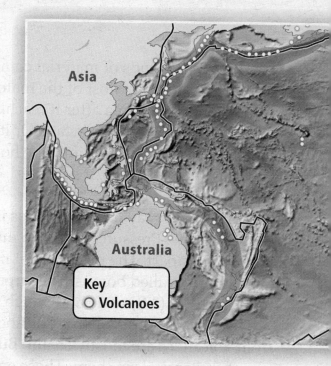

Asia

Australia

Key
○ Volcanoes

Ring of Fire

Many earthquakes and volcanoes occur in an area that borders the Pacific Ocean. For that reason, this area has been named the Ring of Fire.

The Ring of Fire runs around Earth's subduction zones. Subduction zones are places where one of Earth's plates is forced under another. The Pacific Plate converges with several continental plates to form the Ring of Fire.

Faulting during subduction causes earthquakes. It can also lead to volcanic activity. As the subducting plate sinks into the mantle, it melts to form magma. The magma may later rise to the surface as a line of volcanoes.

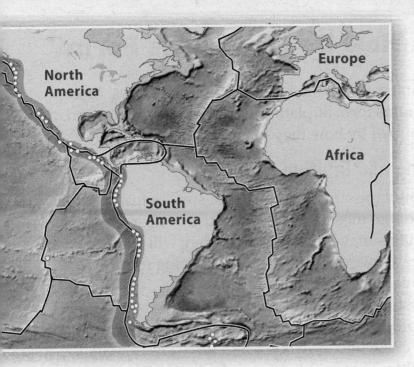

North America

Europe

Africa

South America

On the ocean floor, a deep narrow valley called an ocean trench may form along a subduction zone. Resulting volcanoes often form along the trench, usually along a curved line.

Faulting at diverging boundaries also causes earthquakes and forms volcanoes. Diverging boundaries usually lie near the middle of the deep ocean floor. At these boundaries, magma rises to the surface between separating plates. The rising magma forms volcanic mountain ranges known as ocean ridges. Faulting at the ridges leads to earthquakes.

CAUSE AND EFFECT

What causes magma to rise to the surface of a volcano?

Summary Earthquakes and volcanoes change Earth's surface, usually at plate boundaries.

Why are earthquakes and volcanoes common along the Pacific Rim?

_____

_____

_____

▶ **Cause and Effect** What causes magma to rise to the surface of a volcano?

Cause		Effect
	→	Magma rises to the surface.

Lesson Preview

dome mountains Mountains that form when magma pushes up on Earth's crust but does not break through. *(noun)*

fault-block mountains Mountains that form along fault lines where blocks of rock fall, are thrust up, or slide. *(noun)*

fold mountains Mountains that form where two plates collide and force layers of rock into folds. *(noun)*

VOCABULARY SKILL: Use Diagrams

Diagrams help you understand the meanings of words. Look at the diagram on this page. What do you know about *fold mountains* from the diagram?

_____

_____

_____

GPS **S5E1a.** Identify surface features caused by constructive processes.

---

3 How Do Mountains Form?

Mountains are formed in a few different ways. Most mountains form at plate boundaries. Mountains can be grouped by how they form and by their height.

Folding and Faulting Forces

Mountains are Earth's highest surface features, and some of the most beautiful. Because of their huge size, mountains may seem as though they will be there forever. However, they are always being formed and destroyed.

Most mountains form at or near plate boundaries. Most of the largest mountain ranges form where two plates crash into each other and force layers of rock into folds. These are known as **fold mountains**.

Folding often happens at the edge of a continent. It may result in long, narrow mountain ranges. The Andes in South America is an example.

Faulting can form high cliffs when a large piece of rock is forced upward or downward. This formation in the Rocky Mountains is an example.

Fold mountains often form where an ocean plate crashes into a continental plate. Sediment from the ocean floor becomes attached to the edge of the continent. The sediment and continental rock crumple together, forming rolling folds. As the layers of rock wrinkle, they may also crack. This forms faults, or breaks, in the crust.

Fault-block mountains may form where faulting happens. You know that during faulting, rocks break into blocks at a fault. The blocks may move in several ways along one or more faults to form mountains.

Most fault-block mountains appear to form at converging or diverging boundaries. However, mountain-building also happens at sliding faults. The mountains may split and slip sideways like a stack of magazines falling to one side.

1. Where do most of the largest mountain ranges form?

_____

_____

GPS **CRCT Prep**

Circle the correct answer.

2. The Rocky Mountains are examples of

A. dome mountains.

B. fold mountains.

C. fault-block mountains.

D. volcanoes.

S5E1a

47

I Wonder . . . How does the formation of volcanic mountains at converging boundaries compare with formation at a diverging boundary?

_____

_____

_____

_____

3. Where is the world's largest mountain chain located?

_____

Volcanic Forces

Sometimes volcanic activity forms mountains. This kind of mountain most often forms at plate boundaries.

Volcanic activity may happen at converging boundaries. There, the edge of one plate sinks under another and melts into magma. If the magma rises and bursts through the crust, it generally forms a volcanic mountain.

At diverging boundaries, magma rises up between two plates. It then cools on the surface into ridges, or raised lines, of new plate material. Remember that mid-ocean ridges form on the ocean floor at diverging boundaries. These underwater mountains make up the world's longest mountain chain.

Volcanoes have been called mountains of fire.

A dome mountain forms when magma bulges upward under the crust and hardens as it cools.

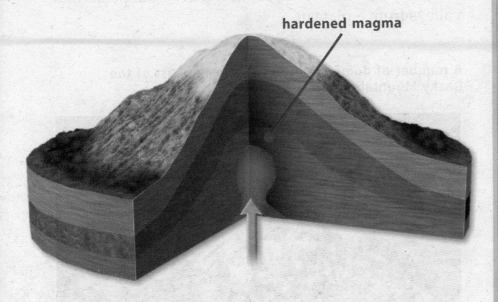

hardened magma

Volcanic mountains can form away from plate boundaries as well. Magma rising in the mantle forms hot spots in the crust. As a plate moves over a hot spot, volcanic material erupts through the plate. Such eruptions form a chain of volcanic mountains. Sometimes magma rises toward the surface but does not break through the crust. It may push up under Earth's crust instead. This forms a dome-shaped mound. The melted rock then cools and hardens. This is how **dome mountains** are formed.

4. Identify each type of mountain and tell how each forms.

a. _____
_____
_____

b. _____
_____
_____

c. _____
_____
_____

49

Summary Mountains are formed by various processes, usually at plate boundaries. They can be classified by how they form and by their height.

What mountain range was formed entirely by erosion?

_____

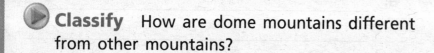 **Classify** How are dome mountains different from other mountains?

Fold	formed where two plates collide and force layers of rock into folds
Dome	
Fault-Block	formed along fault lines where blocks of rock fall, are thrust up, or slide

Erosion often continues to shape dome mountains. Irregular peaks and valleys may result. The Black Hills in South Dakota and the Adirondack Mountains in New York are examples of dome mountains.

Some mountains are formed entirely by erosion. The Catskills in New York are an example. These mountains formed when erosion carved out peaks and valleys from a plateau.

A number of dome mountains lie to the east of the Rocky Mountain range.

CLASSIFY

How are dome mountains different from other mountains?

core (kohr), Earth's innermost structure

crust (kruhst), the thin, rocky outer layer of Earth that makes up the continents and the ocean floor

dome mountains (dohm MOWN tuhnz), mountains that form when magma pushes up on Earth's crust but does not break through

earthquake (URTH kwayk), violent shaking of Earth's crust as built-up energy is released

epicenter (EHP ih sehn tuhr), point on Earth's surface directly above the focus of an earthquake

fault (fawlt), crack in Earth's surface along which movement takes place

fault-block mountains (fawlt blahk MOWN tuhnz), mountains that form along fault lines where blocks of rock fall, are thrust up, or slide

focus (FOH kuhs), point underground where the faulting in an earthquake occurs

Draw a picture that illustrates a science term found on this page.

51

Visit www.eduplace.com to play puzzles and word games.

Choose two or more science words and explain why they go together.

_____
_____
_____
_____

Glossary

fold mountains (fohld MOWN tuhnz), mountains that form where two plates collide and force layers of rock into folds

fossil (FAH suhl), physical remains or traces of a plant or animal that lived long ago

lithosphere (LIHTH uh sfihr), shell formed from Earth's solid upper mantle and crust

magma (MAG muh), melted rock below Earth's surface; called lava at the surface

mantle (MAN tl), thick layer of Earth's structure just below Earth's crust

plate tectonics (playt tehk TAHN ihks), theory that giant plates of crust are moving slowly across Earth's surface

seismic waves (SYZ mihk wayvz), waves of energy sent through Earth's crust when parts of the crust move suddenly

Responding

Think About What You Have Read

 **CRCT Prep**

❶ By studying the wavy lines of a seismograph, scientists can

A. prevent earthquakes.

B. cause earthquakes.

C. ignore earthquakes.

D. measure earthquakes.

S5E1c

Comprehension

❷ What happens when stress builds up along a fault?

❸ Why do earthquakes and volcanoes generally occur at plate boundaries?

❹ Name and describe the four kinds of mountains.

Critical Thinking

❺ Why do tall mountains form at converging and diverging boundaries but not often at sliding boundaries?

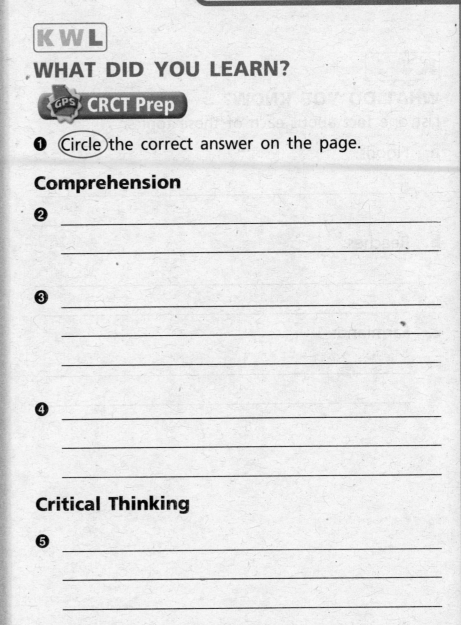

K W L

WHAT DID YOU LEARN?

CRCT Prep

❶ Circle the correct answer on the page.

Comprehension

❷ _____

_____

❸ _____

_____

_____

❹ _____

_____

Critical Thinking

❺ _____

_____

_____

53

WHAT DO YOU KNOW?

List one fact about each of these topics.

a. Floods:

_____

_____

b. Beaches:

_____

_____

c. Farmland:

_____

_____

Managing Earth's Changes

Contents

WHAT DO YOU WANT TO KNOW?

Skim the pictures and headings in this chapter. List one thing you want to find out about each of these topics.

a. How floods are controlled:

_____

_____

b. Ways people protect beaches:

_____

_____

c. How soil forms:

_____

_____

How Can Floods Be Controlled?

VOCABULARY

dam A wall across a river that controls the flow of river water. *(noun)*

flood Occurs when water flows or collects over land that is usually dry. *(noun)*

floodway A prepared path for flood waters to flow over, often to prevent damage to communities. *(noun)*

levee A wall along the banks of a river or other body of water that serves to keep water behind it. *(noun)*

reservoir An artificial lake, often formed when water collects behind a dam. *(noun)*

storm drain A system of pipes or channels that carry away storm water. *(noun)*

VOCABULARY SKILL: Use Pictures
Use clues from the picture on this page to help you understand what the word *flood* means.

A lot of rain for many days can cause a flood. An overflowing river can cause a flood. A very strong storm can cause a flood, too. People have created ways to help control floods. Sometimes, though, these ways cause problems.

Too Much Water

Floods can cause a lot of damage. A **flood** occurs when water flows or collects over land that is normally dry. Floods can destroy buildings. Floods can damage crops. Floods can drown people and animals.

A lot of rain over a short period of time can cause a flood. In Georgia, floods are sometimes caused by hurricanes, which are large storms that bring a lot of rain.

First, the rain goes into the ground. The ground gets very wet. When the ground cannot hold any more water, the water flows over the ground. This is called runoff. A flood forms when there is too much runoff.

Floods can cause a lot of damage.

S5E1c. Relate the role of technology and human intervention in the control of constructive and destructive processes. (flood control)

The Mississippi River before the flood.

The Mississippi River during the flood.

Rivers and Lakes

Floods also form when rivers and lakes get too full. If there is too much rain, the water can spill over a river's banks, or sides.

In 1993, there were very heavy rains in the Midwest. Water in the Mississippi River went over the river's banks. This caused a flood.

In 2005, Hurricane Katrina hit New Orleans. It caused Lake Pontchartrain to break through its banks. The city was flooded.

Flood Damage

Floods cause a lot of damage each year. Floods carry rocks and dirt. They also carry chemicals and waste. All of these things are left behind when the water goes back down.

Floods also damage buildings. Sometimes these buildings cannot be fixed so they must be torn down.

1. What is a flood?

   _____

   _____

   _____

2. List three causes of floods.

   a. _____

   b. _____

   c. _____

3. List four ways that floods cause damage.

   a. _____

   b. _____

   c. _____

4. How does each item help control floods?

   a. wetland: _____

   _____

   b. storm drain: _____

   _____

   c. levee: _____

   _____

GPS **CRCT Prep**

Circle the correct answer.
5. **Sandbags are piled along the banks of a rising river to form a**

   A. temporary levee.

   B. temporary dam.

   C. reservoir.

   D. storm drain system.

S5E1c

Controlling Floods

Nature has its own way of controlling floods. Wetlands often soak up extra water.

People, too, have ways to prevent floods, or at least to make floods less damaging.

Storm Drains Cities use these to help move rain water. **Storm drains** are pipes that carry away storm water. Rain water goes into these pipes. The water enters the pipes through grates. Grates are metal openings on streets or parking lots.

Levees A **levee** is a wall along a river or other body of water. The levee is higher than the river water, so it holds back the water. People have built levees along many rivers. The Mississippi River has over 3,000 miles of levees.

This levee is made of sand bags. It is helping keep water out of homes in a flooded area.

The dam helps control the water in the river.

Dams and Reservoirs A **dam** is a wall across a river. The dam slows down the river water. Soon there is more and more water behind the dam. The water collects into an artificial lake called a **reservoir**.

People can control how much water is in the reservoir. They can let some of the water through the dam. Then the reservoir has less water.

Dams and reservoirs help even out the flow of a river from season to season. For example, snow melts in the spring. Spring rains and melted snow fill the reservoir. The extra water does not flow over the river's banks. In this way, dams and reservoirs help stop floods and allow for a steady water supply all year.

6. Compare and contrast a dam and a levee.

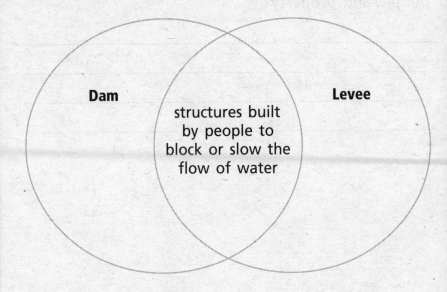

Dam

structures built by people to block or slow the flow of water

Levee

7. Fill in the blanks.

A ——————— is a wall across a river. The water that collects behind the dam is an artificial lake called a ———————.

59

I Wonder . . . How does a floodway protect people and property?

_____

_____

_____

_____

This floodway gives river water a place to go when the river floods.

Floodways In some places, it is difficult to prevent floods. In these places, people sometimes build floodways. A **floodway** is a path for flood waters to flow over.

In 1972, there were floods in Rapid City, South Dakota. Several rivers flooded the area. Buildings were damaged. The city leaders came up with a plan. They bought the land near the rivers. This was the land that often flooded. Most of the buildings were torn down. The land was turned into parks.

Now when the rivers overflow, the water has a place to go. It goes into the floodway. No buildings are damaged.

Should Floods Be Controlled?

Storm drains, levees, dams, and floodways can help prevent floods. However, these can also cause problems.

Levees send extra water down the river. This can cause flooding along other parts of the river, where there are no levees.

Sometimes levees break. After Hurricane Katrina, the levees in New Orleans broke and caused a terrible flood.

Stopping floods can also hurt plants and animals that depend on flood waters. When a river floods, it brings water and soil to the flat lands nearby. This helps the plants and animals.

The Amazon River in Brazil often overflows. The flood water goes into the rainforest. This helps rainforest plants and animals. If a dam were built to stop the flood, it would change life in the rainforest.

Floods from the Amazon River help many plants and animals. Tambaqui feast on seeds they find in the flooded forest.

Tambaqui

8. Fill in the blanks to explain how a dam or a levee can cause problems.

> A dam or levee fails.

> ⬇

> _____ rush through a broken dam or levee.

> ⬇

> This causes _____ and great _____.

9. How do floods help plants and animals that depend on flood waters?

_____

_____

_____

10. What are the Everglades?

_____

_____

11. Explain how Florida's growing population has affected the Everglades.

Cause		Effect
Florida's growing population	→	**a.** People have built _____ and _____. **b.** The Everglades have _____, and the plant and animal populations have _____.

The Everglades

Long ago, the southern part of Florida was covered by huge wetlands. The Everglades were part of these wetlands. In time, people wanted to use the land and water of the wetlands. So levees and canals were built. A canal is a small river built to move water from one place to another. The people of south Florida now have more land and fresh water.

The water is used on farms and in cities. Now dirt and chemicals go into the rivers. This flows to the Everglades. It hurts the plants and animals there. Because of the levees and canals, there is now less water going to the Everglades. The Everglades are smaller than before. There are fewer plants and animals living there.

Today, many of the levees and canals are being taken down. This will help the plants and animals that live in the Everglades.

Too many levees have hurt the Everglades.

Georgia Floods

Georgia has many floods. There are often floods in the northern and southeastern parts of the state. All areas of Georgia, though, can be flooded.

There was a very bad flood in Georgia in 1977. Heavy rain fell. The Toccoa River rose and soon broke through the Kelly Barnes Dam. Great amounts of water rushed through the valley. Many people were killed.

Tropical Storm Albert hit Georgia in 1994. A tropical storm is like a hurricane but smaller. The water in the Flint River went over its banks. The town of Albany was flooded. Thousands of buildings were destroyed.

A flood in Georgia caused this damage.

Summary   Heavy rainfall over many days, overflowing rivers, and severe storms all cause floods. Technology for controlling floods has benefits and drawbacks.

How do floods affect Georgia?

_____

_____

 Summarize   Describe four things that people build to control floods.

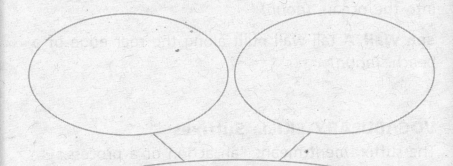

Ways that people control floods.

SUMMARIZE

Describe four things that people build that help to control floods.

barrier island Land formed over many years by the build up of sand and dirt just offshore from the mainland. *(noun)*

beach nourishment The dumping of new sand onto an eroded beach to restore it. *(noun)*

dredging Deepening or widening a river or harbor. *(verb)*

jetty A thin, narrow wall built from the shoreline into the ocean. *(noun)*

sea wall A tall wall built along the rear edge of a beach. *(noun)*

VOCABULARY SKILL: Suffixes
The suffix *-ment* means "an action or a process." Read the definition of *nourishment* above. Based on your knowledge of the word *nourish,* write your own definition for the term *beach nourishment.*

_____

_____

_____

GPS **S5E1c.** Relate the role of technology and human intervention in the control of constructive and destructive processes. (beach reclamation)

2 How Can Beaches Be Protected?

Beaches can get smaller over time. This can happen when they no longer get sand from different places. It can also happen when the ocean washes sand away.

Sandy Beaches and Barrier Islands

Rivers pick up sand and other sediments. The rivers carry these into oceans. The ocean waves then pick up the sand and sediments. The sand and sediments may get dropped along coastlines. When this happens, a sandy beach forms.

Sometimes the sand and sediments are dropped in the ocean, not far from the shore. Over many years, this sand and sediment may build into a new landform called a **barrier island**. There are many barrier islands along the Atlantic coast of the United States. The Golden Isles are Georgia's barrier islands.

Cumberland Island is a barrier island just off the coast of Georgia.

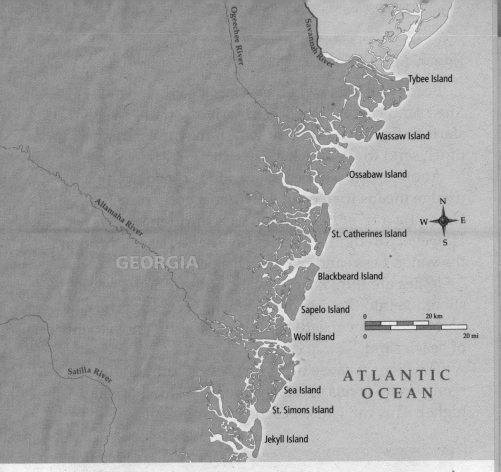

Ogeechee River

Savannah River

Tybee Island

Wassaw Island

Ossabaw Island

N
W — E
S

St. Catherines Island

Altamaha River

GEORGIA

Blackbeard Island

Sapelo Island

| 0 | | 20 km |
| 0 | | 20 mi |

Wolf Island

Satilla River

ATLANTIC OCEAN

Sea Island

St. Simons Island

Jekyll Island

This map shows some of the barrier islands along the Georgia coast.

Beaches are always changing. The beaches of the Golden Isles change every day. That's because waves pick up sand and move it to new places on the beach. Wind blows sand to create small hills called dunes. These dunes also change their size and shape.

Today, some of the eastern beaches of the Golden Isles are getting smaller. Ocean waves are washing away more sand from these beaches than the waves bring in. So over time there is less and less sand on the beaches. These waves are also bringing sand into the marshes, or wetlands, that are west of the islands.

1. Circle the barrier islands that are shown on the map of Georgia.

2. What factors can change a beach from day to day?

   a. _____
   _____

   b. _____
   _____

3. What is a jetty? What is its purpose?

_____

_____

_____

_____

I Wonder . . . How might a dam on a river change ocean beaches near the mouth of the river?

_____

_____

_____

_____

Beach Erosion

Beach erosion is when beaches lose their sand. Most sand comes to beaches by rivers. If the river starts to flow in a different way, it may not carry as much sand to the beach.

Another cause of beach erosion is **dredging**. To dredge means to deepen or widen a body of water. Dredging a river helps boats pass through it. However, dredging changes how sand passes through the water. Less sand may reach a beach.

Jetties are thin, narrow walls built from the shoreline into the ocean. They help keep sand out of harbors. However, jetties can also stop the movement of beach sand.

The biggest cause of beach erosion, though, is rising ocean levels. Oceans have been slowly rising higher. This can cause beaches to erode quickly.

This is a jetty. A jetty can stop sand from reaching a beach.

One way to stop a beach from getting smaller is to dump new sand onto it. This is called **beach nourishment**. This only works for a while, though, because ocean waves carry away the sand. More sand must be dumped onto the beach.

People also use **sea walls** to stop beach erosion. A sea wall is a tall wall built along the rear edge of a beach. When waves come toward the beach, they hit the sea wall. The waves lose much of their energy and cannot carry away as much sand.

Sea walls do not always work. They can also cause problems. So some scientists believe that it is best to leave the beaches alone. In fact, it is a law that some beaches on the Golden Isles in Georgia must be left alone.

Sea walls like this make it harder for waves to carry away sand.

4. Look at the picture of the sea wall on this page. Describe how a sea wall may help protect a beach.

_____

_____

_____

_____

GPS **CRCT Prep**

(Circle) the correct answer.
5. **People build which of these structures to slow beach erosion?**

   A. barrier island

   B. river dam

   C. reservoir

   D. sea wall

S5E1c

Summary Beaches are eroded when their source of sand is blocked or when oceans advance on them.

How do people try to protect beaches?

_____

_____

_____

▶ **Cause and Effect**   How does global warming affect ocean levels?

Cause		Effect
Global warming	→	

Rising Ocean Levels

Scientists believe that Earth is getting warmer and warmer. Data seems to show that Earth's average temperatures have been slowly rising. This is called global warming.

Global warming causes ice and snow to melt in the polar regions. The polar regions are the Arctic and Antarctica. The melting snow and ice is making ocean levels rise.

Not all scientists agree on what is causing global warming. They do know that rising ocean levels can change coastlines. One day the coast of Georgia may look very different than it does today.

If ocean levels keep rising, beaches like this may disappear.

CAUSE AND EFFECT

How does global warming affect ocean levels?

3 How Is Farmland Managed?

Farmers need good soil to grow crops. Soil can erode, or wash or blow away. There are ways to stop soil from eroding.

Soil: An Important Resource

Soil is a natural resource. It is made up of minerals and small rocks, water, gases, and organic matter. The organic matter is called humus. It comes from dead plants and animals.

Soil can be rough or smooth. This depends on the particles, or small pieces, that make up the soil. Rocky soil is rough. Sandy soil is made of small particles.

Georgia has many kinds of soil. Many of Georgia's soils look red. This is caused by iron in the soil. One kind of red soil is called Tifton soil. It is found in southern Georgia. Cotton grows well in Tifton soil.

Rocky soil has large bits of rock.

Sandy soil is made of very hard particles.

Georgia soil is often red because it has iron in it.

VOCABULARY

contour plowing Plowing in curved rows that follow the shape of the land. *(noun)*

soil A natural resource made up of minerals and small rocks, water, gases, and organic matter. *(noun)*

subsoil The layer of soil just below the topsoil. *(noun)*

terrace farming The planting of crops on level sections called terraces. *(noun)*

topsoil The uppermost layer of soil. *(noun)*

VOCABULARY SKILL: Use Pictures
Pictures help you know the meaning of a word. Look at the pictures of *soil* on this page. What do you know about *soil* from these pictures?

_____

_____

_____

 S5E1c. Relate the role of technology and human intervention in the control of constructive and destructive processes.

1. Label each layer of soil.

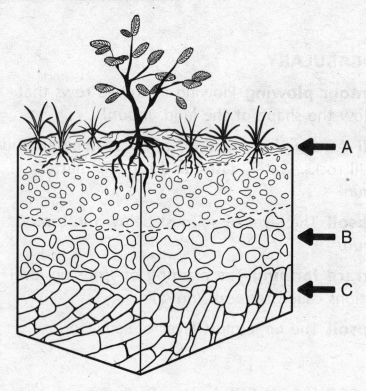

A. _____

B. _____

C. _____

Plants and animals die. Their remains go into the soil. This helps make the soil good for growing plants.

How Soil Forms

Soil starts to form when rocks break into very small pieces. This takes thousands of years. Water, air, and living things make this happen.

There are different layers of soil. **Topsoil** is the surface layer, or the layer we walk on. Topsoil has a lot of humus. Worms and insects live in this layer. They help the soil.

Below the topsoil, there is **subsoil**. Subsoil is not as rich as topsoil. This soil does not have much humus in it. Bedrock is under the subsoil. Bedrock is rock that has not been broken down into small pieces.

Farmers must take good care of topsoil. When topsoil erodes away, it may take many years to form again.

The Dust Bowl

Soil erosion caused big problems for farmers in the Great Plains in the 1930s. During this time there was very little rain. Farmers made mistakes that caused much of their topsoil to blow away.

One mistake farmers made was to plant their crops in long, straight rows. This made it easier to harvest, or collect, the crops. But it also helped the wind blow through the fields more strongly. A lot of loose, dry soil blew away.

In time, the land lost a lot of its topsoil. Strong winds blew dry, loose soil into huge clouds of dust. The area became known as the Dust Bowl.

Without good topsoil, the farmers could not grow good crops. Soon people had little food to eat. Many farmers lost money.

During the Dust Bowl in the 1930s, much of the topsoil blew away.

2. What was the Dust Bowl, and where did it occur?

_____

_____

_____

_____

 CRCT Prep

(Circle) the correct answer.

3. **What helped cause the Dust Bowl of the 1930s?**

A. poor farming practices

B. modern farm conservation

C. contour plowing

D. damp, tightly packed soil

S5E1c

4. List three ways that farmers can protect topsoil.

a. _____

b. _____

c. _____

I Wonder . . . A farmer is trying to plant crops along a steep hillside. What problem does the farmer face? What is a solution?

_____

_____

_____

Contour plowing was used on this field. The rows of crops follow the shape of the land.

Protecting Topsoil

Because of the Dust Bowl, people learned that it was important to protect the topsoil. Scientists have learned ways to do this.

One way to protect the topsoil is called contour plowing. In **contour plowing**, the soil is plowed in curved rows that follow the shape of the land. This slows down the wind. It also helps hold rain water.

Farmers can also hold soil in place by planting cover crops. These are plants that cover loose soil. The soil sticks to the plant roots. The stems and leaves protect the soil from wind.

Soil is often lost as it moves down hills. One way to solve this problem is to use terrace farming. In **terrace farming**, crops are planted on level sections called terraces. Rain water sinks into each terrace. The soil is held in place.

Georgia Farms

Long ago, the farmers of Georgia did not take care of the topsoil. After the Civil War, many poor people called sharecroppers ran farms. They did not own the land so they did not think about caring for the soil. Instead they planted and harvested as many crops as they could. In time, much of the topsoil eroded. The soil went into rivers and reservoirs.

The United States government tried to help. In the 1930s, the Soil Conservation Service was formed. It helped farmers learn how to take good care of the soil.

Farming is still important in Georgia. People keep looking for ways to protect the state's topsoil.

DRAW CONCLUSIONS

Why is it important to protect topsoil?

Summary Farm crops depend on healthy topsoil. Wise practices and techniques prevent soil from eroding.

How has the government helped Georgia protect its soil?

_____

_____

_____

Draw Conclusions Why is it important to protect topsoil?

FACT

↓

FACT

↓

CONCLUSION
It is important to protect topsoil.

73

Glossary

 Visit www.eduplace.com to play puzzles and word games.

Draw pictures illustrating a dam and a levee. Label your drawings.

Glossary

barrier island Land formed over many years by the build-up of sand and dirt just offshore of the mainland.

beach nourishment To dump new sand onto an eroded beach to restore it.

contour plowing When soil is plowed in curved rows that follow the shape of the land.

dam A wall across a river that controls the flow of river water.

dredging To deepen or widen a river or harbor.

flood When water flows or collects over land that is normally dry.

floodway A prepared path for flood waters to flow over, often to prevent damage to communities.

jetty A thin, narrow wall built from the shoreline into the ocean.

Glossary

levee A wall along a river or other body of water that serves to prevent flooding by keeping water behind it.

reservoir An artificial lake, often formed when water collects behind a dam.

sea wall A tall wall built along the rear edge of a beach.

soil A natural resource made up of minerals and small rocks, water, gases, and organic matter.

storm drain A system of pipes or channels that carry away storm water.

subsoil The layer of soil just below the topsoil.

terrace farming When crops are planted on level sections called terraces.

topsoil The uppermost layer of soil.

Circle all the three-syllable vocabulary words found on both pages.

Use *subsoil* and *topsoil* in a sentence that shows the meaning of each word.

_____

_____

_____

Chapter Review

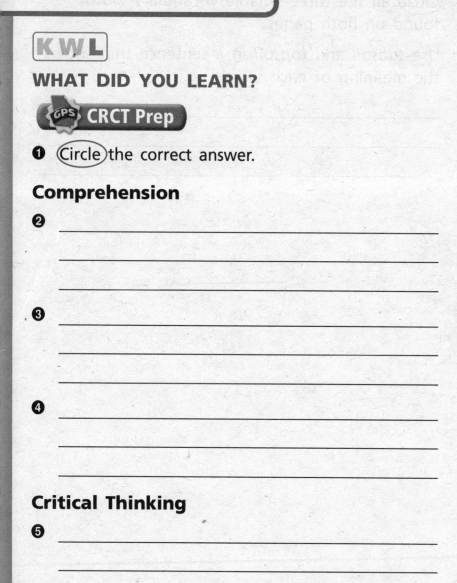

K W L

WHAT DID YOU LEARN?

 **CRCT Prep**

❶ (Circle) the correct answer.

Comprehension

❷ _____

_____

_____

❸ _____

_____

_____

_____

❹ _____

_____

_____

Critical Thinking

❺ _____

_____

_____

Responding

Think About What You Have Read

 **CRCT Prep**

❶ A long wall along the banks of a river is called a(n)

A. reservoir.

B. levee.

C. floodway.

D. jetty.

S5L1a

Comprehension

❷ List three ways that a flood may form.

❸ List three things that would cause a beach to erode.

❹ How does contour plowing help conserve topsoil?

Critical Thinking

❺ Several months after a forest is cut down, a nearby river becomes much muddier than ever before. Infer how the river changed.

KWL

WHAT DO YOU KNOW?

List one fact about each of these topics:

a. What makes up matter:

_____

_____

_____

b. How matter is measured:

_____

_____

_____

c. Physical and chemical properties:

_____

_____

_____

Properties of Matter

Contents

WHAT DO YOU WANT TO KNOW?

Skim the pictures and headings in this chapter. List one thing that you want to find out about each of these topics:

a. States of matter:

_____

_____

_____

b. Mass and weight:

_____

_____

_____

c. Density:

_____

_____

_____

_____

What Makes Up Matter?

Matter is something that has mass and takes up space. Matter can be a solid, a liquid, or a gas.

VOCABULARY

atom The smallest particle of matter that has the properties of that matter. *(noun)*

matter Anything that has mass and takes up space. *(noun)*

molecule A single particle of matter made up of two or more atoms joined together. *(noun)*

physical property A characteristic of matter that can be measured or observed without changing matter into something new. *(noun)*

states of matter The three forms that matter usually takes: solid, liquid, and gas. *(noun)*

VOCABULARY SKILL: Analyzing Word Parts

One way to observe matter is by using a microscope. The word *microscope* is made of two parts: *micro-* and *-scope*. *Micro-* means "small." *-Scope* means "to see." Use this information to describe how a microscope is used.

_____

_____

Looking at Matter

When you look around, you may see things like desks and people. You may feel things you cannot see, like air blowing across your face. Desks, people, and blowing air are examples of matter. **Matter** is anything that has mass and takes up space.

Properties are special qualities for which something is known. Matter has many different properties, such as color, size, shape, and the way it feels. It is easy to see some properties of matter. You may need to use a microscope or hand lens to see other properties.

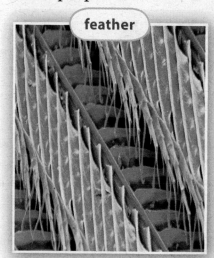 feather

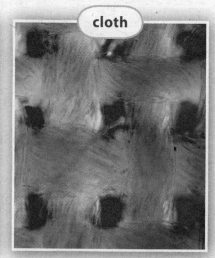 cloth

People use microscopes to make objects look larger. This makes it easier to see an object's properties of matter. Objects can look very different under a microscope.

GPS **S5P1b.** Investigate how common items have parts that are too small to be seen without magnification.

Using powerful microscopes, scientists have learned that all matter is made up of very tiny pieces called particles. The particles are always moving.

The smallest particle of matter that has the same properties of that matter is called an **atom** (AT uhm). All objects are made up of many, many atoms. In fact, there are billions of atoms in a tiny piece of sand!

Most matter is made up of atoms that have joined with other atoms to make a molecule (MAHL ih kyool). A **molecule** is one particle of matter that is made up of two or more atoms joined together. A molecule of water is made up of three atoms.

shampoo

dentist's drill

1. List three things made of matter in your classroom.

a. _____

b. _____

c. _____

2. Compare and contrast atoms and molecules.

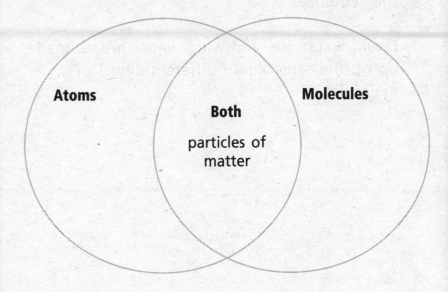

Atoms

Both

particles of matter

Molecules

3. Look at the picture on this page.
   a. Put an X on the liquid water.
   b. Circle an example of solid water.
   c. Which state of water is present but invisible in the picture? _____

4. <u>Underline</u> the phrase that correctly completes this sentence.

   Liquid water, ice, and water vapor are all made up of (the same kind / different kinds) of molecules.

What states of water does this picture show?

Three States of Matter

Matter comes in different forms, or states. The **states of matter** are three forms that matter usually takes: solid, liquid, and gas.

Water looks very different in its three states of matter. Ice is a solid. Water in a pool is a liquid. Water vapor is a gas, which you cannot see. The three states of water look different, but they are all the same kind of matter. Each particle of ice, water, and water vapor is made up of the same kind of molecule. Each molecule is made up of the same three kinds of atoms.

Why do solids, liquids, and gases have different properties? The particles of matter in each of these states are put together in different ways. Look at the chart to understand how.

States of Matter: Water

State of Matter	Molecules	Diagram
Solid The ice frozen on the ground is a solid.	Molecules in a solid are packed close together in a regular pattern.	
Liquid The water in a lake is a liquid.	Molecules in a liquid slide past each other but stay close together. They do not form a regular pattern.	
Water vapor The water vapor in the air is a gas.	Molecules in a gas move quickly and do not stay close together. They do not form any pattern.	

5. Order the three states of water from most closely packed molecules to the most widely spaced molecules.

   liquid water   water vapor   solid water

   a. _____

   b. _____

   c. _____

CRCT Prep

Circle the correct answer.

6. The molecules in a gas
   A. are packed close together.
   B. stay close together.
   C. do not stay close together.
   D. form a regular pattern.

S5P2b

83

7. Complete the table to describe the properties of solids, liquids, and gases.

States of Matter			
State of Matter	Shape	Size	Movement of Particles
a. _____	Always keeps its shape	b. _____ _____	Vibrate slightly
Liquid	c. _____ _____ _____	Fixed size	d. _____ _____ _____
e. _____	Spreads apart or squeezes together to fit into a space	No fixed size	f. _____ _____ _____ _____ _____ _____

Liquid water inside the tea kettle changes to water vapor, a gas that you cannot see above the spout. The cloud that you can see is not a gas. It is made of tiny drops of water mixed with air.

Properties of Solids, Liquids, and Gases

How do you know that water is inside this tea kettle? The cloud you see coming from the spout is a clue. Water turns to steam, then when it hits the cooler air, it condenses to form a cloud of liquid droplets. It changes from one state to another, but it does not become a new kind of matter. The state of matter is a physical property (FIHZ ih kuhl PRAHP ur tee) of matter.

A **physical property** of matter can be seen without changing matter into something new. Size, shape, color, and the way something feels are other physical properties of matter.

You can use the table below to understand the physical properties of solids, liquids, and gases. Remember this about the shapes of different states of matter: A solid always keeps its own shape. A liquid takes the shape of the container it is in. A gas spreads apart or can be squeezed together to fit into spaces.

States of Matter

State of Matter	Shape	Size
Solid	Definite shape	Fixed size
Liquid	No definite shape	Fixed size
Gas	No definite shape	No fixed size

MAIN IDEA

How are ice, water, and water vapor alike?

Summary Matter is anything that has mass and takes up space. Matter may take the form of a solid, a liquid, or a gas. What are three physical properties of matter?

a. _____

b. _____

c. _____

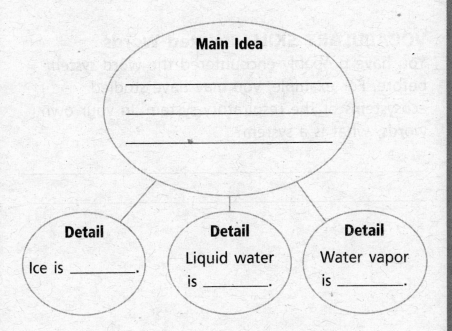

Main Idea How are ice, water, and water vapor alike?

Main Idea

_____

_____

_____

Detail

Ice is _____.

Detail

Liquid water is _____.

Detail

Water vapor is _____.

VOCABULARY

mass The amount of matter in an object. *(noun)*

metric system A system of measurement based on multiples of 10. *(noun)*

volume The amount of space that matter takes up. *(noun)*

weight The measure of the pull of gravity on an object. *(noun)*

VOCABULARY SKILL: Related Words

You have probably encountered the word *system* before. For example, you may have studied ecosystems or the respiratory system. In your own words, what is a system?

_____

_____

GPS S5P1a. Demonstrate that the mass of an object is equal to the sum of its parts by manipulating and measuring different objects made of various parts.

2 How Is Matter Measured?

People use the metric system to measure objects. You can measure objects to find their mass and volume.

The Metric System

Years ago, people came up with a measurement system that everyone could use to measure in the same way. This measurement system helps people talk about matter. The system is called the metric system (MEHT rihk SIHS tuhm). The **metric system** is a system of measurement that uses multiples of 10. Look at the chart on the next page to see how different metric units work together.

Many giraffes grow to be more than 5.5 m tall. How can you find out how tall a giraffe is? You measure it!

A metric ruler measures length in centimeters (cm).

Metric Units Conversion Chart

Type of Measurement	Metric Unit	Converts To
Length	1 centimeter (cm)	10 millimeters (mm)
	1 meter (m)	100 centimeters (cm)
	1 kilometer (km)	1,000 meters (m)
Volume	1 liter (L)	1,000 milliliters (mL)
Mass	1 kilogram (kg)	1,000 grams (g)

On the chart, find the metric units centimeter, meter, and kilometer. These metric units are used to measure length. You can see that 100 centimeters is the same as 1 meter, and 1,000 meters is the same as 1 kilometer. The numbers 100 and 1,000 are multiples of 10. You can change—or convert—to different metric units simply by multiplying or dividing by a multiple of 10.

To measure objects, people use tools that measure in metric units such as centimeters, liters, or kilograms. Length or height can be measured with a ruler that shows centimeters or meters. Mass can be measured using a balance that shows grams or kilograms. The volume of liquids can be measured with a container that shows milliliters or liters.

1. Upon what is the metric system of measurement based? _____

2. Match each tool with what it measures.

balance   liquid volume

ruler   mass

measuring cup   length

3. What is mass?

_____

_____

_____

4. Tell how to use a balance to find the mass of your science book.

> Place the book on one pan.

> Place _____ on the other pan.

> When the pans _____, add the _____ of the standards to find the mass of the book.

Mass

Think about holding two blocks, one in each hand. They are the same size, color, and shape. However, one block feels heavier than the other. To find the difference between the blocks, you can measure their masses. **Mass** is the amount of matter in an object. The block that feels heavier has more mass—and more matter.

All kinds of matter have mass. Mass is a physical property that tells more about an object. Knowing the masses of different objects helps people understand them and sort them into groups. You can use a tool called a balance to measure mass.

This girl is using a balance to measure the mass of a block.

To measure the mass of a block, you put it on one pan of a balance. Then you add objects called standards to the other pan. Standards are objects with known masses. For example, a 1-gram standard has a mass of exactly 1 gram. A 1-kilogram standard has a mass of exactly 1 kilogram.

As you add standards to the other pan of the balance, you watch to see when the two pans balance. When the pans balance, the total mass of the standards is the same as the mass of the block.

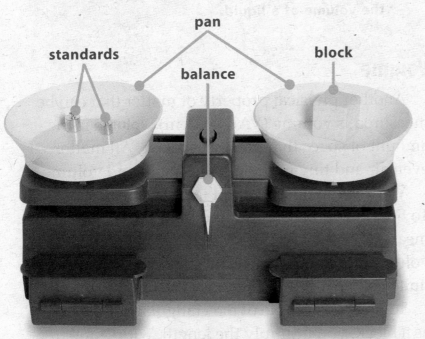

The standards on the left pan of the balance have the same total mass as the block on the right pan.

5. Look at the balance shown on this page. How can you tell that the standards and the block have the same mass?

_____

_____

_____

(Circle) the correct answer.

6. You find the mass of a pack of gum. Then you find the mass of all the sticks and the wrappers. How do these measurements compare?

  A. The two measurements are the same.

  B. The pack has a larger mass than the sticks and wrappers.

  C. The sticks and wrappers have a larger mass than the pack.

  D. The sticks and wrappers have a smaller mass than the pack.

S5P1a

7. (Circle) the tool that is best for measuring the volume of each object.

Measuring Volume	
Item	**Which tool is best?**
a. your science book	ruler or beaker
b. a glass of milk	ruler or beaker
c. your desk	ruler or beaker
d. a mug of hot chocolate	ruler or beaker

To find the volume of a solid like this one, you multiply its length times its width, times its height.

4 cm x 4 cm x 4 cm = 64 cm³

You can use a container called a beaker to measure the volume of a liquid.

Volume

Another physical property of matter that can be measured is volume (VAHL yoom). **Volume** is the amount of space that matter takes up. All matter— even air and tiny particles—has mass and volume.

Volume can be measured in different ways. To find the volume of a liquid, you use a measurement container such as a beaker. The volume of a liquid is measured in the metric units liters (L) and milliliters (mL).

To find the volume of a rectangular solid, such as a block, you multiply the length, width, and height of the block. The volume of a solid is measured in cubic centimeters (cm³).

How do you measure the volume of a solid with a strange shape, such as a rock? First, you put some water in a beaker and write down the volume of the liquid. Then you place the rock into the beaker. The volume of liquid will now be greater. Write down the new water volume.

The change in water volume is the same as the volume of the rock. One milliliter has the same volume as one cubic centimeter. This means that if the water volume in the beaker goes up by 50 milliliters, the volume of the rock is 50 cm^3.

A beaker of water can help you measure the volume of some objects.

8. Tell how to measure the volume of a rock.

Put _____ in a beaker. _____ the amount of water in the beaker.

Put the _____ in the _____.
Record the new _____.

Subtract the _____ volume from the _____ volume. The difference is _____ _____.

I Wonder . . . what can you tell about two objects that have the same volume but different masses?

_____

_____

_____

_____

_____

9. Compare and contrast mass and weight.

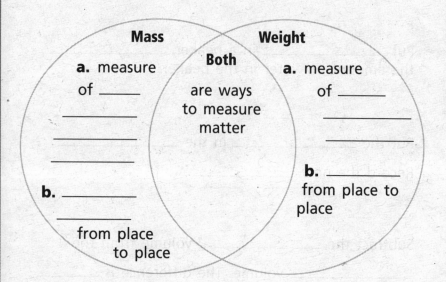

Mass

a. measure of _____

_____

_____

b. _____

_____

from place to place

Both

are ways to measure matter

Weight

a. measure of _____

_____

_____

b. _____

from place to place

Weight

How much does this bear cub weigh? Is its weight (wayt) the same as its mass? No. Mass is the amount of matter in an object. **Weight** is the measure of the pull of gravity on an object.

The bear's mass is the same everywhere it goes. The bear's weight will change as the bear moves to different places on Earth. This is because the amount of gravity pulling on the bear is different in different places.

A spring scale can measure the weight of a bear cub.

At sea level, the bear's weight is a little bit more than its weight on the top of a high mountain. This is because the pull of gravity is stronger at sea level than it is on the top of a mountain. When the bear moves to the top of a mountain, it is farther from the center of Earth. The bear's weight is less on the mountain top because the pull of gravity is weaker there.

On the Moon, the pull of gravity is very weak. A bear would weigh much less on the Moon than it does anywhere on Earth.

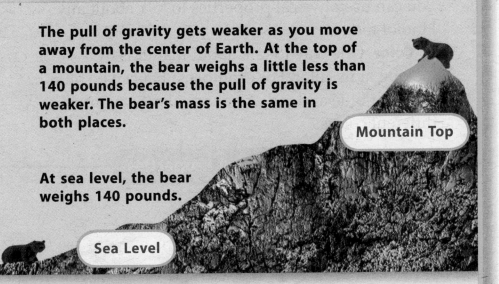

The pull of gravity gets weaker as you move away from the center of Earth. At the top of a mountain, the bear weighs a little less than 140 pounds because the pull of gravity is weaker. The bear's mass is the same in both places.

Mountain Top

At sea level, the bear weighs 140 pounds.

Sea Level

DRAW CONCLUSIONS

How can you find the volume of a block?

Summary Scientists use the metric system to measure objects. Objects can be measured to find their mass, volume, and weight. Circle the place where the person would weigh the least.

Mount Everest

Moon

Sea Level

▶ **Draw Conclusions** How can you find the volume of a block?

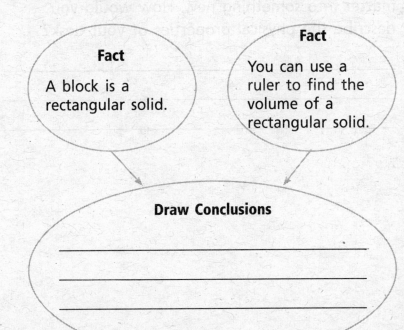

Fact

A block is a rectangular solid.

Fact

You can use a ruler to find the volume of a rectangular solid.

Draw Conclusions

_____

_____

_____

VOCABULARY

chemical property A characteristic of matter that can be observed only when matter is changed into a new kind of matter. *(noun)*

density The amount of matter in a given space, or a given volume. *(noun)*

VOCABULARY SKILL: Reviewing Vocabulary
In Lesson 1 you learned the definition of *physical property*. Recall that a physical property is one that can be measured or observed without changing matter into something new. How would you describe the physical properties of your desk?

_____

_____

_____

S5P2c. Investigate the properties of a substance before, during, and after a chemical reaction to find evidence of change.

3 What Are Physical and Chemical Properties?

Matter has physical and chemical properties. People use physical and chemical properties to describe and sort different types of matter.

Physical Properties

In the morning you might bring your blue backpack to school. At lunch you might eat a big, smooth apple. At night you might sleep on a soft pillow. The words "blue," "big," "smooth," and "soft" all tell about physical properties of matter. You can use physical properties to talk about any kind of matter.

Color One way to talk about matter is by looking at its color. For example, a hat can be blue or red or blue and red. A hat can also be many different colors.

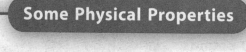

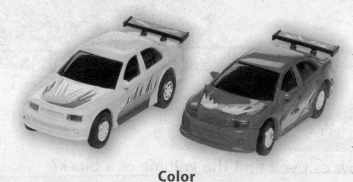

Color

Shape Another way to talk about matter is by looking at its shape. Some things have shapes that are easy to name. The two shapes shown in the picture are a cube and a cylinder. Many things do not have a shape that is easy to talk about. It might be hard to name the shape of objects like your hand, a butterfly, or a leaf.

Texture The texture (TEHKS chur) of an object tells how the object feels. Glass windows have a smooth texture. The trunk of a tree may have a bumpy texture. The two rocks in the picture have different textures. One is smooth. The other is rough.

Luster Luster tells how the outside of an object looks when light shines on it. A mirror is very shiny, but a piece of black construction paper is not shiny.

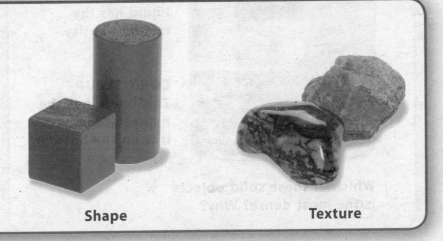

Shape   Texture

1. Look at the objects on these two pages.
   a. Circle all the items that are red.
   b. Put an X on the objects that are hard.
   c. Draw a box around an object with a rough texture.
   d. Draw a star on the object with a shiny luster.

2. Describe an object that has a physical property that is *not* shown on these two pages.

_____

_____

_____

95

3. Circle the item that has the greater density in each pair.
   a. liter of corn syrup

      liter of water

   b. cubic centimeter of steel

      cubic centimeter of cotton

4. Which solid object shown in the glass has the greatest density? How do you know?

   _____

   _____

   _____

I Wonder . . . Do all objects that are the same size have the same density?

   _____

   _____

   _____

Density Another physical property of matter is density (DEHN sih tee). **Density** tells how much matter is in a certain space, or volume. For example, one cubic centimeter of rock has more mass than one cubic centimeter of cotton. That means that rock is more dense than cotton.

The density of an object makes it float or sink in a liquid like water. If something is more dense than water, it will sink. If it is less dense than water, it will float.

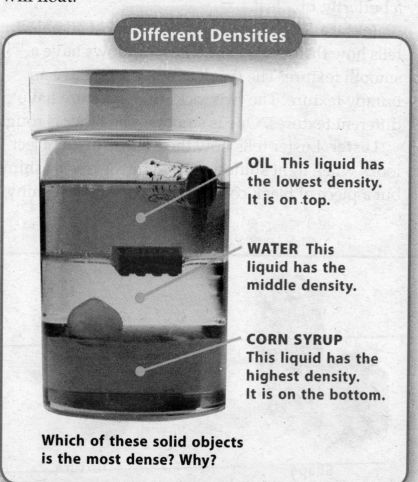

Different Densities

OIL This liquid has the lowest density. It is on top.

WATER This liquid has the middle density.

CORN SYRUP This liquid has the highest density. It is on the bottom.

Which of these solid objects is the most dense? Why?

Useful Physical Properties

Each kind of matter has its own set of physical properties. These physical properties help people choose how to use each kind of matter.

You would not use ice to make a chair. It would melt in a warm room. The physical properties of wood and metal make these kinds of matter better for making a chair. The chair would be strong and it would keep its shape in a warm or cold room.

Physical properties that make matter useful in one way do not always make it useful in another way. Glass is clear and smooth. Its physical properties make it useful for making windows. But ordinary glass would not be useful for making safety glasses. It breaks too easily.

This desk top is made from foam rubber. What will happen when the boy puts the books on it?

5. List a physical property of each type of matter. Tell how that property makes matter useful.

a. wood: _____

_____

b. cotton: _____

_____

c. glass: _____

_____

6. Define *chemical property.*

_____

_____

_____

GPS CRCT Prep

Circle the correct answer.

7. **A scientist has a sheet of paper. After an experiment, the paper has turned to ash. The scientist is investigating**

   A. density.

   B. mass and weight.

   C. chemical changes.

   D. physical changes.

S5P2c

Chemical Properties

Look at the pictures of the burnt log and the cut log. The logs have different physical properties, such as size, shape, and texture.

You cannot burn a burnt log, but you can burn a cut log. Something that can be burned has a property of matter called a chemical (KEHM ih kuhl) property. A **chemical property** can be seen only when matter is changed into a new kind of matter. You can see the chemical property of wood as it burns and becomes ash. Ash is a different kind of matter than wood.

Cut logs can burn. They have a chemical property because they can change into a different kind of matter by burning.

Burnt logs—or ash—cannot burn again. They do not have the chemical property that allows them to burn.

Describing Chemical Properties

When you cook an egg in a frying pan, heat changes the raw egg into something different—a cooked egg. The fact that the egg can change into a new kind of matter when it is heated is a chemical property. The heat does not change the pan into new matter. It just warms the pan. The pan has had a physical change, not a chemical change.

Matter can change in different ways when it meets air, heat, and water. Chemical properties can help you sort matter into groups. Some metal will get rusty when it gets wet, but it will not burn. Wood will not get rusty, but it will burn easily. Metal and wood do not have the same chemical properties.

When you cook an egg, new matter forms.

Summary Matter has different physical and chemical properties. Physical and chemical properties are used to describe and classify matter.

In the picture on this page, which material is ndergoing a chemical change—the egg or the pan?

_____

▶ **Compare and Contrast** How is a chemical property different from a physical property?

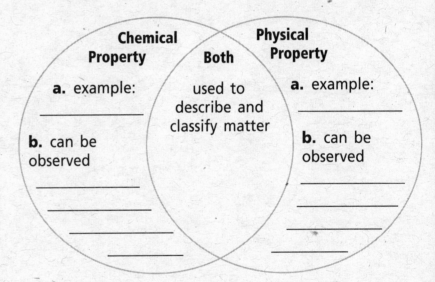

Chemical Property
a. example:
_____
b. can be observed
_____
_____
_____

Both
used to describe and classify matter

Physical Property
a. example:
_____
b. can be observed
_____
_____
_____

COMPARE AND CONTRAST

How is a chemical property different from a physical property?

Glossary

Review the glossary terms shown on these two pages. List four terms that describe a physical property of matter.

a. _____

b. _____

c. _____

d. _____

Glossary

atom (AT uhm) The smallest particle of matter that has the properties of that matter.

chemical property (KEHM ih kuhl PRAHP ur tee) A characteristic of matter that can be observed only when matter is changed into a new kind of matter.

density (DEHN sih tee) The amount of matter in a given space, or a given volume.

mass (mas) The amount of matter in an object.

matter (MAT ur) Anything that has mass and takes up space.

metric system (MEHT rihk SIHS tuhm) A system of measurement based on multiples of 10.

Glossary

molecule (MAHL ih kyool) A single particle of matter made up of two or more atoms joined together.

physical property (FIHZ ih kuhl PRAHP ur tee) A characteristic of matter that can be measured or observed without changing matter into something new.

states of matter (stayts uhv MAT ur) The three forms that matter usually takes: solid, liquid, and gas.

volume (VAHL yoom) The amount of space that matter takes up.

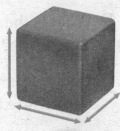

weight (wayt) The measure of the pull of gravity on an object.

 Visit www.eduplace.com to word games and play puzzles.

Complete the word web about states of matter.

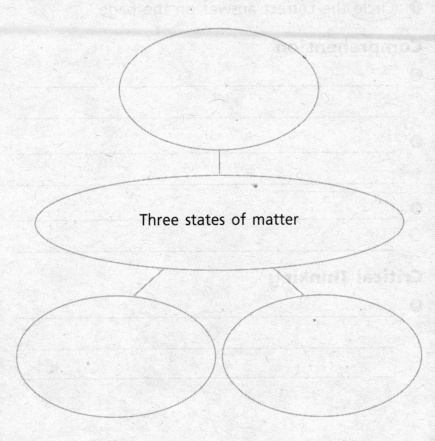

Three states of matter

KWL

WHAT DID YOU LEARN?

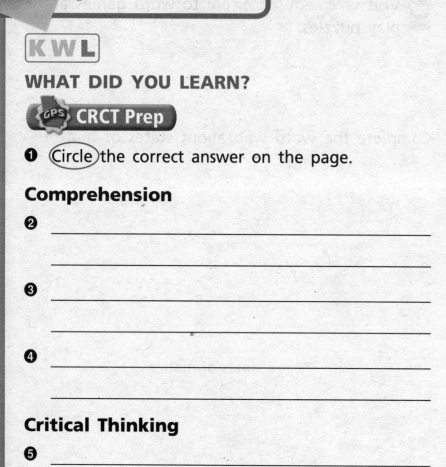

CRCT Prep

❶ Circle the correct answer on the page.

Comprehension

❷ _____
_____

❸ _____
_____

❹ _____
_____

Critical Thinking

❺ _____
_____
_____

Responding

Think About What You Have Read

CRCT Prep

❶ **Mass is a measure of**

　A. the amount of space an object takes up.

　B. how fast the particles in an object move.

　C. the amount of matter in an object.

　D. the pull of gravity on an object.

Comprehension

S5P1b

❷ What is the difference between an atom and a molecule?

❸ What units would a scientist most likely use to measure the length of a small object?

❹ What are some physical and chemical properties of paper that can be seen?

Critical Thinking

❺ Compare the mass of a person on Earth with the mass of the same person on the Moon. Then compare the weight of a person on Earth with the weight of the same person on the Moon.

WHAT DO YOU KNOW?

List one fact about each of these topics:

a. Physical changes in matter:

_____

_____

b. How matter changes when heated or cooled:

_____

_____

c. Mixtures and solutions:

_____

_____

d. Chemical changes in matter:

_____

_____

How Matter Changes

Contents

WHAT DO YOU WANT TO KNOW?
Skim the pictures and headings in this chapter. List one thing that you want to find out about each of these topics:

a. Common physical changes:

_____

_____

b. How matter changes state:

_____

_____

c. Common mixtures:

_____

_____

d. Common chemical changes:

_____

_____

VOCABULARY

energy The ability to cause change. *(noun)*

physical change A change in the size, shape, or state of matter that does not change it into a new kind of matter. *(noun)*

VOCABULARY SKILL: Multiple-meaning Words

The word *physical* has several meanings. You may know it as a noun meaning "an examination by a doctor." In this lesson, *physical* is an adjective that describes a kind of change in matter. Look through the lesson at the pictures of physical changes. Then write your own definition of physical change.

_____

_____

S5P2a. Investigate physical changes by separating mixtures and manipulating (cutting, tearing, folding) paper to demonstrate examples of physical change.

1 What Are Physical Changes in Matter?

Physical changes are changes in size, shape, or state. Physical changes do not make new kinds of matter form. Energy is a part of all changes in matter.

Size, Shape, and State

Suppose you are playing baseball with your friends. You hit the ball and it cracks a window of your house. The glass breaks into hundreds of tiny pieces. Your baseball has caused a physical change in the window glass. A **physical change** changes the way matter looks. It does not change it into a new kind of matter.

Many physical changes change the size, shape, or state of matter. The shape and size of the window glass changed when it broke, but each piece of broken glass still had the properties of glass. No new kinds of matter were formed.

The shape and size of the candy changes when it is hit with the hammer. The other properties of the candy stay the same.

The juice bar changes from a solid to a liquid as it melts. This is a change in state. Changes in state are physical changes.

Look at the melting juice bar. The melted part looks different from the frozen part. If you tasted the melted part of the juice bar, it would taste the same as the frozen part. The melted juice bar is not a new kind of matter. It still tastes like a frozen juice bar. It has just changed from a solid to a liquid. This change in state is a physical change.

If you hit the juice bar with a hammer, how would it change? The juice bar would probably break into smaller pieces, like the candy in the picture. The smaller pieces might melt, but new kinds of matter would not be formed.

1. List three ways in which physical changes change matter.

   a. _____

   b. _____

   c. _____

2. Look at the picture of the candy on page 106. What are two things about the candy that will be the same before and after the hammer hits it?

   a. _____

   b. _____

I Wonder . . . When a puddle of water evaporates, does the water change into a new kind of matter?

_____

_____

_____

3. Define *energy*.

_____

_____

4. Tell what provides the energy for each physical change listed below.

a. ball breaking a window:

_____

_____

b. paper being cut into the shape of a snowflake:

_____

_____

c. water evaporating from a puddle:

_____

_____

Common Physical Changes

Look at the picture below. The student has cut and drawn on the paper and shaped the clay. You know that these changes are physical changes. They are physical changes because the paper and clay have not been changed into something new.

When matter is moved or changed, energy (EHN ur jee) is at work. **Energy** is the ability to cause change. Sometimes energy must be added to matter to make it change. For example, heat must be added to ice so the ice will melt. Heat is a form of energy. Heat is added to a glue stick in a hot glue gun. The glue stick melts when heat is added.

This student has made physical changes to the clay and paper.

Sometimes matter gives off energy when it changes. If you bend a metal paper clip back and forth many times, the clip will begin to feel warmer. That is because heat energy is given off as you bend it.

Think about physical changes that happen every day. Ice melts. Glass breaks. You cut some paper. These changes in form, size, and shape need energy. Heat energy from the Sun melts the ice. The energy of a moving baseball breaks the glass. The energy in your body helps you cut out a snowflake.

Summary   Physical changes involve a change in size, shape, or state. No new kinds of matter are formed. All changes in matter involve energy. How do you know that the changes the student is making on page 108 are physical changes?

_____

_____

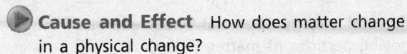 **Cause and Effect**   How does matter change in a physical change?

Cause		Effect
A physical change occurs.	→	Matter changes _____ without changing into a new kind of matter.

109

VOCABULARY

heat The flow of thermal energy from a warmer area to a cooler area. (noun)

temperature A measure of how hot or cold matter is. (noun)

thermal energy The total kinetic energy of tiny moving particles of matter. (noun)

VOCABULARY SKILL: Synonyms and Antonyms

In this lesson, you will learn that matter is made of particles that are always in motion. Look at the words below.

movement   motion   stand still

Movement and *motion* are synonyms. *Motion* and *stand still* are antonyms. Write what you think synonyms and antonyms are on the lines below.

Synonyms:

_____

Antonyms:

_____

S5P2b. Recognize that the changes in state of water (water vapor/steam, liquid, ice) are due to temperature differences and are examples of physical change.

2 What Happens When Matter Is Heated or Cooled?

Heating and cooling matter changes the way its particles move and the amount of space between the particles.

Thermal Energy and Matter

Suppose you have a small box and some marbles. You fill just the bottom of the box with a tight layer of marbles. If you shake the box lightly, the marbles might move a little, but they will not move very much. They are packed too tightly together to spread out. The marbles are like particles in a solid. When the marbles move, they have just a little bit of energy of motion.

You could say that the marbles have very little thermal energy (THUR muhl EHN ur jee). **Thermal energy** is the total energy of the particles of matter. It has to do with the energy of moving particles. The particles of a solid have very little energy of motion.

Solid Iron

The particles in this piece of solid iron are packed tightly together. They have very little energy of motion.

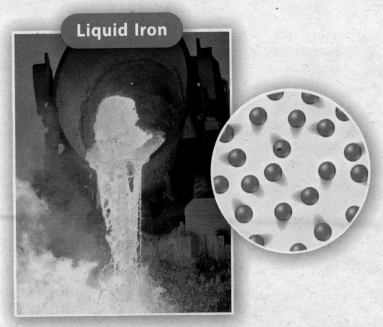

Liquid Iron

The particles of liquid iron are farther apart than the particles of solid iron. This change of state happens because thermal energy has been added to the iron.

If you shake the box of marbles harder, you add more energy to the marbles. The marbles will move apart farther and faster. Particles of matter move like this. If you add more energy to particles of matter, they will move faster and farther apart.

Thermal energy can be added and taken away from matter. You cannot see thermal energy, but you can feel it as heat. **Heat** (heet) is the flow of thermal energy from a warmer area to a cooler area.

When you heat matter, its thermal energy grows. The particles of matter move faster and farther apart. When you cool matter, you take away thermal energy. The particles of matter slow down and move closer together.

1. (Circle) the word that correctly completes each sentence to tell whether thermal energy is added or taken away.

   a. When a cup of warm water is put in the refrigerator, thermal energy is (added to/ taken away from) the water.

   b. When the Sun shines on a parking lot, thermal energy is (added to/taken away from) the parking lot.

   c. When solid iron is melted, thermal energy is (added to/taken away from) the iron.

2. Draw an arrow to tell how heat would move

   cup of hot chocolate   your cold hands

111

3. Underline the word that correctly completes each sentence.

a. When thermal energy is added, particles move (faster/slower) and (farther apart/closer together).

b. When thermal energy is taken away, particles move (faster/slower) and (farther apart/closer together).

Circle the correct answer.

4. The total energy of the particles of matter is called

   A. expansion.

   B. contraction.

   C. thermal energy.

   D. heat.

S5P2b

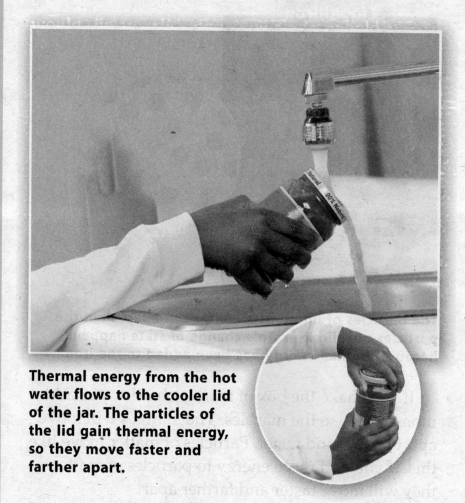

Thermal energy from the hot water flows to the cooler lid of the jar. The particles of the lid gain thermal energy, so they move faster and farther apart.

Look at the picture above. Have you ever tried to open a jar with a tight lid? If you heat a metal jar lid with hot water, its particles move faster and farther apart. The lid gets larger, or expands, and loosens from the jar. If you cooled the lid, it would cause the particles to move more slowly and get closer together. The lid would get tighter, or contract, on the jar.

Temperature

On a snowy day, the air outside is much colder than the air inside your house. You can find out how much colder by measuring the air temperature (TEHM pur uh chur). **Temperature** is used to measure how hot or cold matter is. Temperature also tells how fast the particles of matter are moving. Particles of matter move more slowly in cold temperatures and faster in warm temperatures.

A thermometer (thur MAHM-ih tur) is a tool that measures temperature. Thermometers measure temperature in units called degrees. Scientists and people in some countries use the Celsius (SEHL see-uhs) scale of degrees. In the United States, temperature is measured using the Fahrenheit (FAR-uhn hyt) scale.

You can read a thermometer to know how warmly to dress.

5. (Circle) the matter in which temperature would be higher and particles of matter would be moving faster.

iced tea	hot tea
hot chocolate	chocolate milk
outside air on a snowy day	outside air on a summer day

6. List two scales for measuring temperature.

a. _____

b. _____

I Wonder . . . Your parent puts a cold thermometer under your tongue to take your temperature. Why do the particles in the thermometer begin to move faster?

_____

_____

_____

_____

7. Look at the picture on this page. Draw arrows to show how heat is moving. Then describe the heat movement below.

_____

_____

This picture was taken with a special camera that makes heat look red in the picture. It shows that thermal energy is moving from warm parts of the house to the cooler outside air. The outside air gets warmer as the inside air gets cooler.

When you add heat to an object, its temperature will go up. As you cook, you add heat to food. The heat goes into the food. The food gets warmer and has a higher temperature.

How can you lower the temperature of an object? Remember that heat is the flow of thermal energy from a warmer place to a cooler place. To lower the temperature of an object, you must put it in a cooler place, such as a refrigerator or freezer. Heat will move out of the warmer object into the colder air inside the refrigerator or freezer.

Changes in State

The temperature of matter makes it a solid, liquid, or gas. When matter is heated or cooled, its temperature changes, and it changes state. Melting, freezing, boiling, and condensation are physical changes in the state of matter.

When heat is added to matter, the particles of matter move faster and farther apart. Particles in a solid are held in place close together. When you heat a solid, its particles move faster and faster until they break out of their places. This change in state is melting—a solid becoming a liquid.

Over time, parts of this floating piece of ice will melt. When ice melts, water changes from a solid to a liquid. This is a physical change.

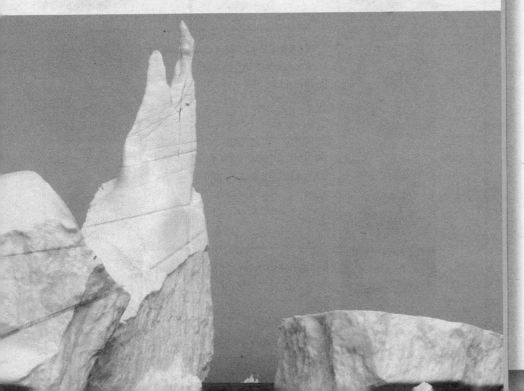

8. List four changes of state.

   a. _____

   b. _____

   c. _____

   d. _____

GPS CRCT Prep

(Circle) the correct answer.

9. **What kind of change is a change in state?**

   A. physical change

   B. chemical change

   C. particle change

   D. matter change

S5P2b

115

10. Tell what happens when you add heat to each item.

Adding Heat

Item	What happens?
a. a wax candle	_____ _____
b. a frozen fruit pop	_____ _____
c. a pot of water	_____ _____

Particles in a liquid can move past each other, but they stay close together. When you heat a liquid, its particles move faster and faster until they spread even farther apart. The liquid becomes a gas during a change in state called evaporation. Particles in a gas move quickly and there is much space between them. At very high temperatures, liquid evaporates quickly. Boiling is very fast evaporation.

Change the State

Starting State of Matter	Change	Ending State of Matter
Solid	**Melting** Adding thermal energy to turn a solid into a liquid	Liquid
Liquid	**Freezing** Taking away thermal energy to turn a liquid into a solid	Solid
Liquid	**Boiling** Adding thermal energy to turn a liquid into a gas	Gas
Gas	**Condensation** Taking away thermal energy so a gas or vapor cools and turns into a liquid	Liquid

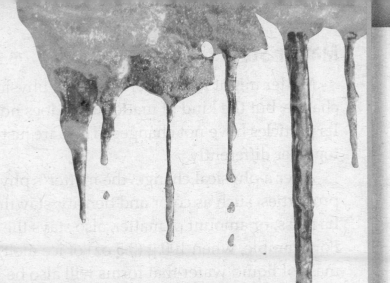

The particles of this ice are gaining thermal energy. What change in state is happening to the ice?

If you take heat away from matter, it will change in state again. The particles of matter will move more slowly and closer together. As matter cools, gases turn into liquids—or condense. Liquids can also turn into solids—or freeze.

Changes in state are physical changes. The matter looks different, but it is not a new kind of matter. In changes of state, the matter looks different because the particles of matter are in different places. The particles have not changed. The particles of ice are the same as the particles of liquid water. They are just packed together in different ways.

Particles that are held together more strongly, such as in solids, need more energy to break them apart.

11. Tell what happens when you take away heat from each item.

Taking Away Heat	
Item	**What happens?**
a. cup of orange juice	_____
	_____
b. water vapor (gas)	_____
	_____

12. Order the states of matter from particles that are closest together to particles that are farthest apart.

gas   liquid   solid

_____

13. How do particles change during a change of state?

_____

_____

_____

I Wonder . . . If 100 grams of water evaporate into a gas, how much mass will the gas have?

_____

_____

_____

Matter Stays the Same

Matter might look different after a physical change, but the kind of matter itself does not change. Its particles have not changed. They are just packed together differently.

After a physical change, the matter's physical properties, such as color and density, stay the same. Its mass, or amount of matter, also stays the same. For example, when 100 g (3.5 oz) of ice melt, the mass of liquid water that forms will also be 100 g.

This man is using thermal energy to make iron soft.

Water is not the only kind of matter that changes state. Metals, such as iron, can also change state. When iron is heated, it gets soft. Soft metals can be hammered and bent into different shapes. When you add more heat, the metal gets softer and softer. Finally, it melts into a liquid. It has changed state, but its physical properties are still the same. It is not a new kind of matter.

Look at the pictures. The man is changing hot, soft iron into different shapes. The iron cools and hardens into its new shape—a gate.

Summary Heating and cooling matter changes the motion of its particles and the spacing between them. What tool is used to measure temperature, or how hot or cold an object is?

_____

▶ **Classify** Classify each of the following changes according to whether they are caused by adding heat or taking heat away: boiling, condensation, melting, freezing.

Adding Heat	Taking Heat Away

VOCABULARY

dissolve To mix completely with another substance to form a solution. *(verb)*

mixture Matter made up of two or more substances or materials that are physically combined. *(noun)*

solution A mixture in which the particles of one kind of matter are mixed evenly with the particles of other kinds of matter. *(noun)*

VOCABULARY SKILL: Applying Vocabulary

Read the definitions of *mixture* and *solution*. The forming of mixtures and solutions is a physical change. What do you know about the matter that makes up mixtures and solutions, now that you know the forming of mixtures and solutions is a physical change?

_____

_____

3 What Are Mixtures and Solutions?

Mixtures and solutions are made up of two or more things—or substances—that are put together during a physical change.

Mixtures

What is at the bottom of your backpack? It could be pencils, paper clips, and papers mixed together, or combined. This combination of things is a mixture (MIHKS chur). A **mixture** is matter made up of two or more substances that are physically combined.

Making a mixture is a physical change. The pencils, paper clips, and papers are all mixed up, but their physical properties have not changed. The pencils are still pencils.

It would be easy to separate the substances, or sort them into groups, by looking at their different physical properties. When substances in a mixture are very different, it is easier to separate them. Separating the parts of a mixture is a physical change.

This mixture of tiny pieces of iron and sand is easy to separate by using a magnet.

S5P2a. Investigate physical changes by separating mixtures and manipulating (cutting, tearing, folding) paper to demonstrate examples of physical change.

This machine can separate a mixture of coins into groups of coins with the same size.

You cannot separate all mixtures by hand. Some mixtures can be separated using a change in state. To separate a mixture of sugar and water, you could boil it. The water would change to a gas, or evaporate, and only the sugar would be left.

Different densities can also be used to separate a mixture. Density is a physical property of matter, like mass and volume. Soil could be separated into its parts by mixing it with water and letting the mixture rest. The most dense soil parts, like stones, would sink first. The less dense soil parts, like sand or clay, would sink later.

1. List three ways to separate mixtures.

a. _____

b. _____

c. _____

2. Imagine that you have a mixture of sugar and water.

a. You cannot see the sugar in the mixture. How could you test to see whether the sugar is still there?

_____

_____

b. What would happen if you heated the mixture?

_____

_____

_____

121

3. List three common mixtures.

a. _____

b. _____

c. _____

4. Circle any mixtures listed in question 3 in which not all the parts can be seen.

Some Common Mixtures

There are mixtures everywhere. Bubbles are a mixture of soap and water. A bowl of soup is a mixture. Your sock drawer holds a mixture of socks. Mixtures can be any combination of matter. Some mixtures are solids, liquids, and gases together. Other mixtures have just solids, just liquids, or just gases.

In mixtures like soup, it is easy to see the separate parts. You can see carrots in some places and noodles in other places. You can see that the substances in soup still have their physical properties.

In other mixtures, you cannot see the separate parts. In lemonade, you cannot see the water, lemon juice, and sugar that make up the mixture. These separate parts cannot be seen, but they still have their own physical properties.

You cannot see the separate substances, but these bubbles are a mixture of soap and water.

Look for mixtures in the picture below. Some mixtures are easier to see than others. Fog is a mixture of air and water. Air is a mixture of gases. Sea water is a mixture of water and salts. The lighthouse is made of many different mixtures. Concrete is a mixture. The glass and metal parts are mixtures. Even the paint on the lighthouse is a mixture.

Fog is a mixture of air and water.
Air is a mixture of gases.

5. List four mixtures shown in the photo on this page.

a. _____

b. _____

c. _____

d. _____

I Wonder . . . How is a mixture such as a plate of pasta with sauce and meatballs different from a mixture such as air?

_____

_____

_____

_____

6. Circle the mixture that is easier to separate. Put an X on the mixture that is also a solution.

sand and water

salt and water

Solutions

A mixture of sand and water looks different from a mixture of salt and water. You can see the particles of sand in the first mixture. You cannot see the particles of salt in the second mixture. If you taste it, you know the salt is still there.

Salt water is a mixture called a solution (suh LOO shun). In a **solution**, the particles of one kind of matter are mixed evenly with the particles of other kinds of matter. The whole solution has the same properties.

A Liquid Solution: Sea Water

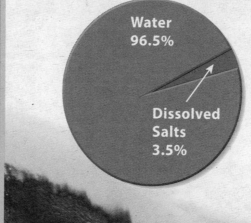

Water 96.5%

Dissolved Salts 3.5%

Sea water is the most common liquid solution on Earth. Every 1,000 g of sea water is made up of 965 g of water and 35 g of dissolved salts.

You are looking at salt under a microscope!

You cannot see the salt in salt water because it has dissolved. To **dissolve** (dih ZAHLV) means to mix completely with another substance by separating into particles that you cannot see.

As salt dissolves in water, the particles of water circle around the particles of salt. The water particles and salt particles move together. After time, the solid salt is broken down into particles that are mixed evenly with water particles. When this happens, you cannot see the salt.

The properties of a solution are often different from the properties of its separate parts, but dissolving is a physical change. The physical properties of the parts of the solution stay the same.

A solution can be separated back into its parts, but not by hand. When the water evaporates from a salt water solution, the salt is left behind.

8. What must happen in order for a solution to form?

_____

_____

I Wonder . . . When salt dissolves in water, does the salt change its state?

_____

_____

_____

_____

9. Define solubility.

_____

_____

10. List two things that can affect the solubility of a substance.

a. _____

b. _____

11. Look at the pictures on this page.

a. Put an X on the beaker in which the material is _not_ soluble.

b. Circle the beaker in which all the material has dissolved.

Solubility

Sand is not soluble in water. No particles of sand are dissolved in this beaker of water.

Salt is more soluble in water than sand. Some salt has sunk to the bottom of the beaker.

Sugar is very soluble in water. All of the sugar has dissolved in the water.

Comparing Solutions

Look at the mixtures in the glass beakers. The same amount of solid was added to equal amounts of water in each one. Some solids dissolve in water better than others. Solubility (sahl yuh BIHL ih tee) is a measure of how much of a substance can dissolve in another substance. The solubility of a substance changes in different temperatures and different substances.

Look again at the three beakers. If you add sand to a beaker of water, all of the sand will sink to the bottom of the beaker. Sand is not soluble in water. Sand particles cannot separate and mix with water particles.

Salt and sugar are both soluble in water at room temperature. You can see that sugar is more soluble than salt.

Because solutions are mixtures, it does not matter exactly how much of each part is mixed together. A solution of salt water can have a lot of salt and taste very salty. Or, it can have only a little salt and taste only a little salty. Both mixtures are solutions of salt water.

Summary Mixtures and solutions are made up of two or more substances that are combined during a physical change. Compare and contrast mixtures and solutions.

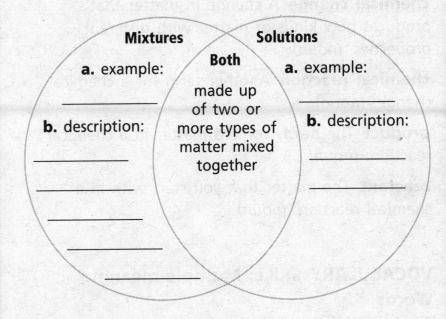

Mixtures

a. example:

_____

b. description:

_____

_____

_____

_____

Both

made up of two or more types of matter mixed together

Solutions

a. example:

_____

b. description:

_____

_____

▶ **Text Structure** Where in the text of this lesson would you find examples of common mixtures?

_____

_____

TEXT STRUCTURE

Where in the text of this lesson would you find examples of common mixtures?

VOCABULARY

chemical change A change in matter that produces new kinds of matter with different properties. *(noun)*

chemical reaction Another term for a chemical change. *(noun)*

product The newly formed matter in a chemical reaction. *(noun)*

reactant The matter that you start with in a chemical reaction. *(noun)*

VOCABULARY SKILL: Multiple-meaning Words

Read the definition of *chemical change*. The word *produce* has several meanings. Say the word with the accent on the second syllable. When said this way, *produce* means "make." Say the word with the accent on the first syllable. The word now refers to fruits and vegetables. Write a sentence that uses one of these meanings of *produce*.

_____

_____

GPS **S5P2c.** Investigate the properties of a substance before, during, and after a chemical reaction to find evidence of change.

---

4 What Are Chemical Changes in Matter?

A chemical change makes new kinds of matter.

New Matter

Do you like waffles? Waffles are made using a mixture of flour, sugar, oil, and eggs. Can you taste the eggs in waffles? Not really. As you cook the waffles, the properties of the flour, sugar, oil, and eggs change. That is why you cannot taste the eggs. Cooking the waffles is not a physical change. It is a chemical change.

A **chemical change** is a change in matter that makes new kinds of matter with different properties. A chemical change needs energy. Energy is given off or taken in during a chemical change. When you make waffles, the flour, sugar, oil, and eggs take in energy to form a new kind of matter—a waffle!

Cooking is a chemical change that changes the parts of waffle batter into new matter—the waffles.

A burning fire is a chemical change that gives off heat and light, which are two kinds of energy.

Particles of matter—atoms and molecules—are part of physical changes and chemical changes. During a physical change, atoms and molecules move. During a chemical change, molecules break apart and mix in different ways with other atoms and molecules. This forms new matter with different properties. The atoms and molecules mix in new ways during a chemical reaction (ree AK shuhn). A **chemical reaction** is a chemical change.

In a chemical reaction, the matter that you start with is called the **reactant** (ree AK tuhnt). When you make waffles, the reactants are flour, sugar, oil, and eggs. The **product** of a chemical reaction is the new matter that forms. Waffles are the product when you cook the waffle batter.

1. Circle the term that comes first in a chemical change.

   product

   reactant

2. Look at the objects on page 128.
   a. Circle the reactants.
   b. Put an X on the products.

I Wonder . . . What is the difference between the way particles behave in a physical change and the way they behave in a chemical change?

_____

_____

_____

_____

129

3. List four clues that signal a chemical change.

   a. _____

   b. _____

   c. _____

   d. _____

4. What kind of energy is most often present during a chemical change?

_____

_____

Common Chemical Changes

    Chemical changes are everywhere. Cars burn gas in a chemical reaction that makes energy to move the car. Burning wood and rusting metal are also chemical changes. Your body uses chemical reactions to change food into the molecules and energy you need to grow.

    Thermal energy is the kind of energy most often found during chemical changes. It can be added or taken away. Light, electricity, sound, and motion are other kinds of energy that can be found during chemical changes.

    Bubbles and changes in color, state, temperature, smell, and energy tell you that a chemical change is happening. The biggest sign of a chemical change is that new products form that have properties that are different from those of the reactants.

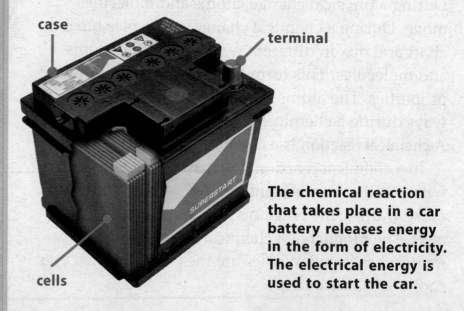

case

terminal

cells

The chemical reaction that takes place in a car battery releases energy in the form of electricity. The electrical energy is used to start the car.

Two reactants are mixed together inside a glow stick. This makes a chemical reaction that makes the liquid inside the stick light up—or glow.

How does a chemical change take place? Atoms and molecules are held together by forces called chemical bonds. During a chemical reaction, the chemical bonds are broken. New bonds form between different atoms and molecules. This causes new matter, or products, to form. The new products are made up of different atoms and molecules, so they have different properties from the reactants.

Energy is often given off during a chemical reaction. This energy can warm a house, start a car, or light up a dark room. Sometimes the energy that is given off can be dangerous. The energy can make something blow up. This can wreck buildings and hurt people.

5. List the steps that occur as a chemical change takes place.

a. Atoms and molecules are held together by

_____.

b. During a chemical reaction, the _____

are _____.

c. _____ form between different atoms

and molecules.

d. New _____ form. The properties of

these _____ are different from the

properties of the reactants.

6. Compare and contrast chemical and physical changes.

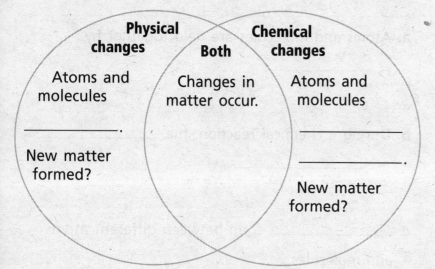

Comparing Physical and Chemical Changes

You have learned about physical and chemical changes in matter. In a physical change, no new matter is formed. The matter might look different, but the chemical bonds between the particles of matter have not been broken. A pool of water that freezes into solid ice goes through a physical change.

In a chemical change, a new kind of matter always forms. The new matter looks different and has different physical properties. This is because the chemical bonds between the particles of the reactants have been broken. New bonds have formed. A piece of wood that burns into ash goes through a chemical change.

A Chemical Reaction: Medicine in Water

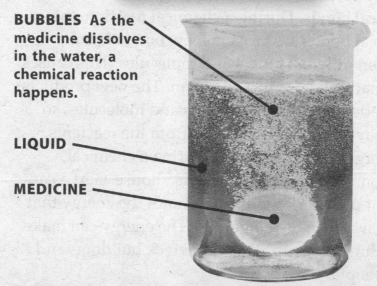

BUBBLES As the medicine dissolves in the water, a chemical reaction happens.

LIQUID

MEDICINE

Bubbles tell you that a chemical reaction is taking place.

Comparing Changes in Matter

Physical Changes	Chemical Changes
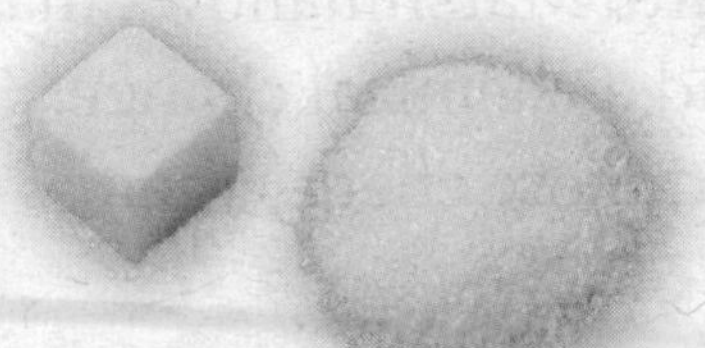 Crushing a sugar cube does not change the kind of matter. Tiny pieces of sugar are still sugar.	 Sticky caramel is sugar that has been burned. Heat changes the sugar particles into new matter—caramel.
 Folding paper does not break chemical bonds. No new bonds are formed. Folded paper is still paper.	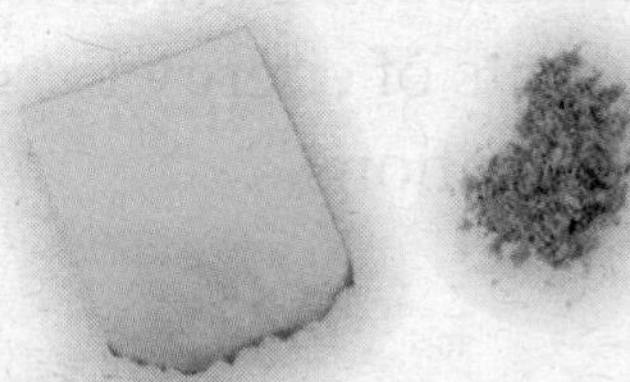 When paper is burned, it turns to ash.
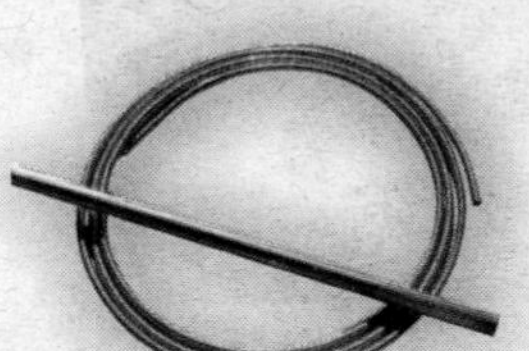 It is easy to bend copper. Bending a copper tube does not break chemical bonds. Copper is still copper.	 Water in the air mixes with the copper in this penny to form a green coating.

7. Circle the type of change that generally takes more energy.

   physical change

   chemical change

Circle the correct answer.

8. A bicycle left in the rain rusts. What kind of change is this?

   A. physical change

   B. chemical change

   C. energy change

   D. change of state

S5P2c

133

Summary   A chemical change produces new kinds of matter. Complete the diagram to summarize changes in matter.

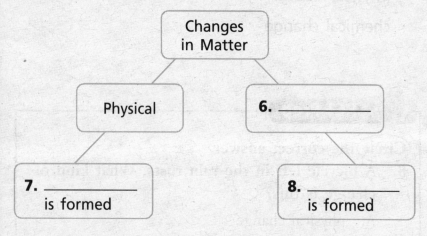

Changes in Matter
- Physical
  - 7. _____ is formed
- 6. _____
  - 8. _____ is formed

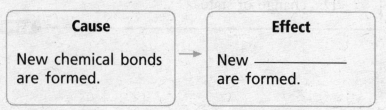

Cause and Effect   What happens when new chemical bonds are formed?

Cause		Effect
New chemical bonds are formed.	→	New _____ are formed.

Have you ever cooked a marshmallow over a fire? Cooking a marshmallow can make it warm and soft or brown and hard. It takes more time and more heat from the fire—more energy—to make a marshmallow brown and hard. Marshmallows that are brown and hard have had a chemical change. Chemical changes often need more energy than physical changes.

It also takes energy to separate physical and chemical combinations. Physical combinations are mixtures like sugar water. Chemical combinations, or chemical compounds, are combinations of atoms that are held together by chemical bonds. Sugar is a chemical compound. It takes different kinds and amounts of energy to separate physical and chemical combinations.

CAUSE AND EFFECT

What happens when new chemical bonds are formed?

134

chemical change (KEHM ih kuhl chaynj) A change in matter that produces new kinds of matter with different properties.

chemical reaction (KEHM ih kuhl ree AK shuhn) Another term for a chemical change.

dissolve (dih ZAHLV) To mix completely with another substance to form a solution.

energy (EHN ur jee) The ability to cause change.

heat (heet) The flow of thermal energy from a warmer area to a cooler area.

mixture (MIHKS chur) Matter made up of two or more substances or materials that are physically combined.

Circle the terms on this page that result in a physical change.

Visit www.eduplace.com/gascp to play word games and puzzles.

Write a sentence telling how reactants and products are related.

_____

_____

_____

Glossary

physical change (FIHZ ih kuhl chaynj) A change in the size, shape, or state of matter that does not change it into a new kind of matter.

product (PRAHD uhkt) The newly formed matter in a chemical reaction.

reactant (ree AK tuhnt) The matter that you start with in a chemical reaction.

solution (suh LOO shuhn) A mixture in which the particles of one kind of matter are mixed evenly with the particles of other kinds of matter.

temperature (TEHM pur uh chur) A measure of how hot or cold matter is.

thermal energy (THUR muhl EHN ur jee) The total kinetic energy of tiny moving particles of matter.

Responding

Think About What You Have Read

CRCT Prep

1. During a chemical change, ________ are broken and reformed.

   A. molecules

   B. forms of energy

   C. reactants

   D. products

S5P2c

Comprehension

2. How does heating affect particles of matter?

3. What is a solution? Give an example of a solution.

4. How are new kinds of matter formed in a chemical change?

Critical Thinking

5. A friend tells you that baked cookies are exactly the same matter as the dough used to make them. Discuss this idea and explain whether you think it is true or false.

Chapter Review

KWL

WHAT DID YOU LEARN?

CRCT Prep

1. Circle the correct answer.

Comprehension

2. ____

____

3. ____

____

4. ____

____

Critical Thinking

5. ____

____

____

Electricity and Magnetism

KWL

WHAT DO YOU KNOW?

List one fact about each of these topics:

a. Static electricity:

Static electricity can shook you from touching somebody or something.

b. Electric current:

Electricity comes from power and the electricity heats up your water.

c. Magnets:

Magnets can push away from each other and stick to each other called repelling and attracting.

d. Electromagnets:

Electromagnets can push trains and all kinds of big and heavy stuff.

Contents

WHAT DO YOU WANT TO KNOW?

Skim the pictures and headings in this chapter. List one thing that you want to find out about each of these topics:

a. Electric charges:

I want to learn what electric charges are.

b. Electric circuits:

I want to learn what electric circuits are.

c. Magnetic fields:

d. Motors:

139

electric charges Tiny particles that carry units of electricity. *(noun)*

static electricity An electric charge that builds up on a material. *(noun)*

VOCABULARY SKILL: Use Illustrations

Read the definition of *electric charges*. These charges can be described as negative or positive. Scan the information on this page. Write the symbols for negative charges and positive charges in the space below.

Positive Charges:

Negative Charges:

---

1 What Is Static Electricity?

All matter is made up of tiny particles. Some have a positive electric charge. Some have a negative charge.

Electric Charges

Have you ever felt a shock from a doorknob after walking on a carpet? Here's why. You know that all matter is made up of tiny particles called atoms. Doorknobs and carpet are made of atoms. Atoms are made up of even tinier particles. Many of these tiny particles carry units of electricity called **electric charges**. These charges gave you the shock.

There are positive ⊕ electric charges and negative ⊖ electric charges. Charges that are the same are called like charges. Charges that are different are called unlike charges. Most matter is electrically neutral. Electrically neutral means matter has an equal number of positive and negative charges.

ELECTRICALLY NEUTRAL
Matter that has the same number of positive and negative charges

NEGATIVELY CHARGED
Matter that has more negative than positive charges

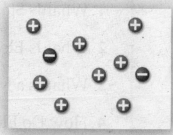

POSITIVELY CHARGED
Matter that has more positive than negative charges

S5P3a. Investigate static electricity.

How Charges Behave

Electric charges can act on each other, even without touching. Like charges repel. They push away from each other. Unlike charges attract. They pull toward each other. Two objects with like charges push away from each other. Two objects with unlike charges pull toward each other.

Negative charges are attracted to positive charges. Particles that have a negative charge can move more easily from one material to another than particles with a positive charge can. So negative charges tend to move toward matter that is positively charged.

Negative charges do not usually move toward an electrically neutral object. However, negative charges can be made to move. Rubbing can move negative charges from one electrically neutral object to another.

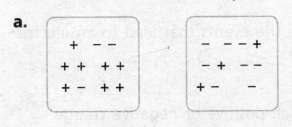

Rubbing a balloon with a wool cloth causes negative charges to move from the cloth to the balloon.

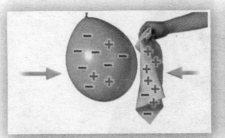

UNLIKE CHARGES ATTRACT
When brought close together, objects with unlike charges attract each other.

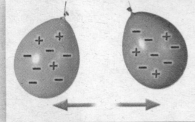

LIKE CHARGES REPEL
When brought close together, objects with like charges repel each other.

1. Identify the charge on each sample of matter.

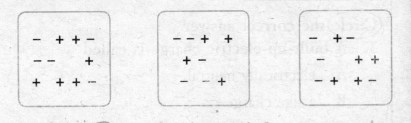

a. _positive_   b. _Negative_   c. _neutral_

2. Draw arrows to show whether the two objects in each set will attract or repel.

a.

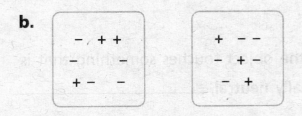

b.

Circle the correct answer.

3. A built-up electric charge is called

   A. electrically neutral.

   B. a like charge.

   C. static electricity.

   D. an unlike charge.

S5P3a

4. Sequence the events that lead to an electric discharge.

a. An overall positive or negative charge

_____.

b. When the object touches something that is electrically neutral, _____

_____.

142

Buildup and Discharge

Sometimes an electric charge builds up on a material. This built-up electric charge is called **static electricity** (STAT ihk ih lehk TRIHS ih tee). When your hair stands on end and moves toward a plastic comb, you can see static electricity at work.

Running a comb through your hair moves negatively charged particles from your hair onto the comb. Your hair loses negative charges and has an overall positive charge. The comb gains negative charges and now has an overall negative charge.

Your hair and the comb now have unlike charges. They attract each other. Each hair on your head now has a like charge. They repel each other. The result is they stand on end and push away from each other.

You sometimes get a shock when you touch a metal doorknob. The shock is caused by a release of electric charges. In the picture, the boy's body has built up a negative charge. When he touches the doorknob, the charge quickly jumps from him to the doorknob. This release of the built-up negative charge is called an electric discharge, or spark.

electric discharge

❸ **Shock!** The boy reaches for the metal doorknob. There is a discharge of static electricity.

❷ The boy's body becomes negatively charged.

❶ Rubbing against the carpet causes negative charges to build up on the boy's shoes.

CAUSE AND EFFECT

How do like charges act on each other? How do unlike charges act on each other?

Summary All matter is made up of tiny particles, some of which carry positive or negative electric charges. Objects can be neutral or have a negative or a positive charge. What causes the buildup of like charges?

_____

_____

▶ **Cause and Effect** How do like charges act on each other? How do unlike charges act on each other?

Cause		Effect
Like charges come near each other.	→	_____ _____

Cause		Effect
Unlike charges come near each other.	→	_____ _____

143

Lesson Preview

VOCABULARY

conductors Materials that negatively charged particles can move through easily. *(noun)*

electric cell A device that turns chemical energy into electrical energy. *(noun)*

electric circuit The pathway that an electric current follows. *(noun)*

electric current A continuous flow of electric charges. *(noun)*

insulators Materials that electric charges do not flow through easily. *(noun)*

parallel circuit A circuit in which the parts are connected so that the electric current passes along more than one pathway. *(noun)*

series circuit A circuit in which the parts are connected so that the electric current passes through each part along a single pathway. *(noun)*

VOCABULARY SKILL: Word Meaning

Read the definition for *series circuit*. What does a series circuit have in common with a series of books?

_____

_____

_____

S5P3b. Determine the necessary components for completing an electric circuit.

2 What Is Electric Current?

Electric charges can move if they have a complete pathway to follow.

How Charges Move

You know that when charged particles build up on matter, static electricity is produced. The charges in static electricity might stay in place. Or they might jump to another material in a sudden electric discharge. This kind of energy is not very useful. For the energy of moving charged particles to be useful, the energy must be controlled.

Charged particles can be made to move, or flow, instead of building up. The energy of these particles can be controlled and used. The constant flow of electric charges is called **electric current**. You can use electric current to toast a piece of bread.

Toasting Bread

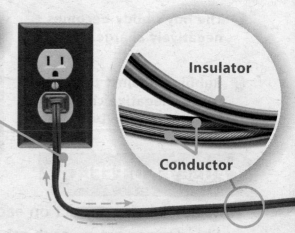

❶ When the toaster is turned on, electric charges flow out of the outlet. The charges move through one copper wire in the cord to heating coils in the toaster.

Insulator

Conductor

Conductors and Insulators

Negatively charged particles move easily through materials called **conductors** (kuhn DUHK tuhrz). Electric current easily passes through some metals. Metals such as copper and silver are good conductors. Water and living things are also good conductors.

Materials that electric charges do not flow through easily are called **insulators** (IHN suh lay tuhrz). Materials such as plastic and rubber are good insulators. Conductors and insulators are used to control and direct electric flow.

A power cord has conductors and insulators. A power cord controls and directs the flow of electric current. A power cord usually has metal conductors. These wires carry electric current. They are inside a rubber or plastic insulator. The insulator keeps the electric current from escaping.

2 Charges move through the heating coils and cause them to get hot. The heated coils toast the bread.

3 Charges return to the outlet through the other wire.

1. Compare and contrast static electricity and electric current.

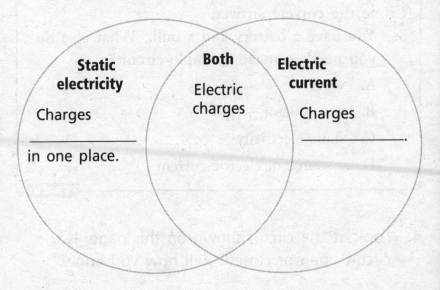

Static electricity

Charges

_____

in one place.

Both

Electric charges

Electric current

Charges

_____.

2. List two conductors and two insulators.

   a. Conductors: _____

   _____

   b. Insulators: _____

   _____

CRCT Prep

Circle the correct answer.

3. **You have a battery and a bulb. What else do you need to make a simple circuit?**

   A. wires

   B. an insulator

   C. static electricity

   D. a source of electric current

S5P3b

4. Look at the circuit shown on this page. Is the circuit open or closed? Tell how you know.

_____

_____

_____

146

Circuits and Switches

The pathway that electric current follows is called an **electric circuit** (ih LEHK trihk SUR kiht). A circuit is a closed pathway. A closed pathway does not have any gaps, or openings. Another name for a closed pathway is a complete pathway.

You can make a simple circuit. You just need wire, a battery, and a light bulb. When you connect these items without gaps, you create a closed circuit. When charges flow through the closed circuit, the light bulb will light.

If there is a gap, or opening, in the circuit, it is an open circuit. A circuit with gaps is also known as an incomplete circuit. When a circuit has gaps, electric charges cannot complete the path. The light bulb will not light.

Simple Circuit

When parts of a circuit connect with no openings, the bulb lights.

Simple Circuit With a Switch

switch

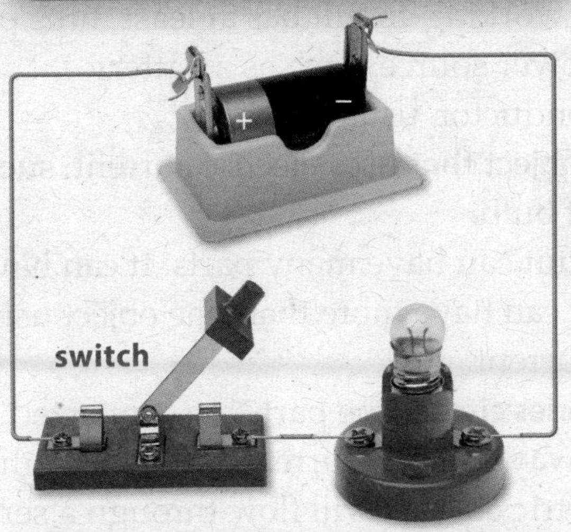

A switch is used to open and close a circuit without disconnecting the wires.

Most circuits have a switch that opens and closes the circuit. A switch lets you turn a light bulb on and off. When you flip the switch on, you close the circuit. The light bulb goes on. When you flip the switch off, you open the circuit. The light bulb goes off.

Some electrical objects are run by batteries. A battery is made up of one or more electric cells. An **electric cell** is an object that changes chemical energy into electrical energy. A flashlight is battery-powered. It is also an example of a simple circuit with a switch.

5. Circle the words that correctly complete each sentence.
  a. Flipping a switch on (opens / closes) a circuit.
  b. Flipping a switch off (opens / closes) a circuit.

I Wonder . . . Why do most circuits have switches?

_____

_____

_____

_____

6. List the three parts that every working circuit has.

a. _____

b. _____

c. _____

7. Identify the circuits shown here.

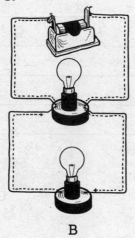

A

B

a. Circuit A is a _____ circuit.

b. Circuit B is a _____ circuit.

Two Types of Circuits

Every working circuit has at least three parts:
- A power source, such as a battery
- A conductor, usually wire
- An object that uses electric current, such as a light bulb.

But a circuit can have many parts. It can have a switch. It can have more than one object using the electric current.

In a **series circuit**, the parts are connected in just one pathway. Electric current flows through each part. Electric current will flow through a series circuit only if all the parts are connected.

In a **parallel circuit**, the parts are connected in more than one pathway. Electric current can flow through all the parts in many ways. Electric current will flow through a parallel circuit even if all the parts are not connected.

Circuit Pathways

SERIES CIRCUIT
If you take one part out, it makes a gap. Electric current cannot move through any of the parts.

PARALLEL CIRCUIT
If you take one part out, electric current can still move through the other parts.

This house uses parallel circuits. The circuit for the kitchen is broken, but current can still pass to the other rooms.

Electricity in the Home

The electric wiring in a house is connected in parallel circuits. If the circuit for one room is broken, electric current can still go to the circuits in the other rooms. The circuits are connected to a main source of electric current in a circuit box.

If too much electric current flows through a circuit, the wires can get too hot. Home circuits have a way to keep the house safe. In the circuit box are circuit breakers. A circuit breaker is a switch. If the circuit gets too hot, the switch opens and breaks the circuit.

COMPARE AND CONTRAST

What is the difference between a series circuit and a parallel circuit?

Summary   Electric charges can move if they have a complete pathway to follow. What device helps keep homes safe from an overheating circuit?

_____

▶ **Compare and Contrast**   What is the difference between a series circuit and a parallel circuit?

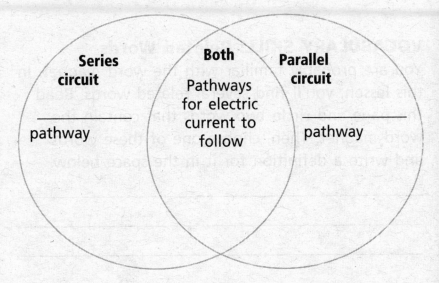

Series circuit

_____
pathway

Both

Pathways for electric current to follow

Parallel circuit

_____
pathway

VOCABULARY

magnet An object that attracts certain metals, mainly iron. *(noun)*

magnetic poles The two areas on a magnet with the greatest magnetic force. *(noun)*

VOCABULARY SKILL: Related Words

You are probably familiar with the word *magnet*. In this lesson, you'll find several related words. Read this page and circle two words that contain the word *magnet*. Then, choose one of these words and write a definition for it in the space below.

_____

_____

_____

3 What Is a Magnet?

A magnet is an object that attracts certain metals. A magnet has a magnetic field. A magnet has magnetic poles.

Properties of Magnets

A **magnet** (MAG niht) is an object that attracts some metals. A magnet mainly attracts iron. This property of magnets to attract metal is called magnetism. Magnetism is stronger the closer a magnet is to an object with iron in it. The closer the magnet gets, the stronger the pull becomes.

Magnets do not attract all metals. Magnets do not attract materials such as wood or rubber. Some magnets keep their magnetism a long time. You can use these magnets to magnetize other objects. But these kinds of magnetized objects lose their magnetism after a while.

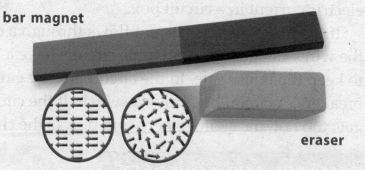

bar magnet

eraser

Particles of matter act like tiny magnets. When particles of an object line up, the object is a magnet.

UNLIKE POLES ATTRACT
The north pole of one magnet pulls toward the south pole of another magnet.

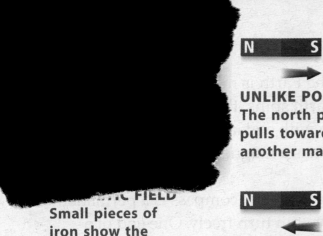

...IC FIELD
Small pieces of iron show the lines of force around a magnet.

LIKE POLES REPEL
The south pole of one magnet pushes away from the south pole of another magnet.

Magnetic Fields

Magnetism is a force. The space in which a magnet's force can act is called its magnetic field (mag NEHT ihk feeld). Each magnet has two **magnetic poles** where the magnet's force is greatest. Look at the picture of a magnetic field. The pieces of iron are thicker and closer together at each end of the bar magnet.

When a bar magnet can swing freely, one end always points north. This end of the magnet is its north pole. The other end points south. This is its south pole.

Remember what you learned about electric charges. Opposite charges attract each other. Magnets act the same way. The unlike poles of two magnets attract each other. The like poles of two magnets repel each other.

1. You put a magnet near a pile of coins. None of the coins is attracted to the magnet. What can you conclude about the metal that makes up coins?

_____

2. Circle the magnetic poles on each bar magnet shown on this page.

3. Tell whether each set of magnets will attract or repel.

A   B

a. Set A will _____.
b. Set B will _____.

151

Summary A magnet is an object that attracts certain metals. A magnet has a magnetic field and magnetic poles. In which direction does the needle of a compass always point?

_____

 Main Idea and Details What will happen if you bring the unlike poles of two magnets near each other?

Main Idea
The poles of magnets interact.

Detail
Like poles will repel and push away from each other.

Detail
Unlike poles will
_____
_____.

Earth as a Magnet

The center of the Earth is m____ melted iron. As Earth spins, t___ up. Imagine Earth with a gia___ This means Earth has a magne___ around it.

The needle of a magnetic compass is a permanent magnet. The needle can turn freely. One end of a compass needle always turns to find north. That is how people can use compasses to know which direction is north. Sailors use magnetic compasses to find their way across oceans.

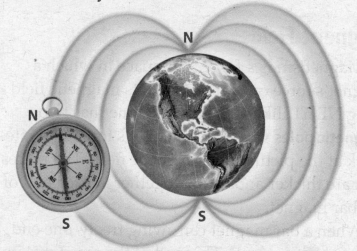

EARTH'S MAGNETIC FIELD
Earth acts like a giant magnet. A compass always points toward Earth's magnetic north pole.

MAIN IDEA AND DETAILS

What will happen if you bring the unlike poles of two magnets near each other?

4 How Do Electromagnets Work?

Magnetism can produce electricity. Electricity can produce magnetism. Together, magnetism and electricity can produce energy of motion.

Electromagnets

An **electromagnet** (ih lehk troh MAG niht) is a strong temporary magnet. It uses electricity to produce magnetism. How does electricity produce magnetism?

You know electric current flows through a conductor, such as a wire. As it flows, it creates a magnetic field around the wire. This magnetic field is weak. If the wire is wrapped around a piece of iron, the iron becomes magnetized. The magnetic field becomes stronger.

Many things in your home have electromagnets in them. Small electromagnets are inside such things as blenders, computer disk drives, and doorbells.

When this circuit is closed, electric current flows through the wire. The nail acts as an electromagnet.

VOCABULARY

electromagnet A strong temporary magnet that uses electricity to produce magnetism. *(noun)*

generator A device that uses magnetism to convert energy of motion into electrical energy. *(noun)*

motor A device that changes electrical energy into energy of motion. *(noun)*

VOCABULARY SKILL: Prefixes

The prefix *electro-* in *electromagnet* means "electricity." Now that you know this, write your own definition for *electromagnet*.

_____

_____

1. List the parts of an electromagnet. Look on page 153 if you need help.

a. _____

b. _____

c. _____

Look on page 153 if you need help.

GPS CRCT Prep

Circle the correct answer.

2. What makes an electromagnet different from a bar magnet?

A. Only an electromagnet attracts materials made of iron.

B. Only an electromagnet can be turned on and off.

C. Only a bar magnet has a magnetic field.

D. Only a bar magnet has poles.

S5P3d

3. Circle the word that will make the sentence true.

To increase the strength of an electromagnet, you can wrap (more / less) wire around the iron core.

Using Electromagnets

Like other magnets, electromagnets attract materials made of iron. They also have magnetic fields. Electromagnets can be very small. Some can fit in your hand. Even small electromagnets can be very strong.

The magnetic force of an electromagnet can be controlled. You can make its magnetic field stronger. If more wire is wrapped around iron, the electromagnet becomes stronger. If more electric current flows through the wire, the electromagnet becomes stronger.

An electromagnet can be turned on and off. It only acts like a magnet when electric current flows through the wire. When the electric current is turned off, the electromagnet loses its magnetism. Electromagnets are very useful. A crane uses an electromagnet to pick up cars and other heavy objects that contain iron.

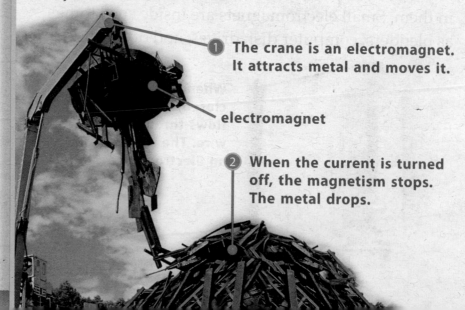

1 The crane is an electromagnet. It attracts metal and moves it.

electromagnet

2 When the current is turned off, the magnetism stops. The metal drops.

Motors

An electric **motor** is a machine that changes electrical energy into energy of motion. All electric motors have electromagnets and permanent magnets.

In an electric motor, wires are wrapped around an iron core called a shaft. Electric current runs through the wires. The shaft becomes an electromagnet. Around the electromagnet is a permanent magnet.

Remember what you know about magnetic fields. Like poles repel. Unlike poles attract. The magnetic fields of the electromagnet and the permanent magnet attract and repel. This creates the energy of motion.

How a Motor Works

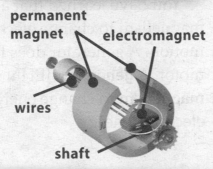

permanent magnet

electromagnet

wires

shaft

① In a motor, electricity flows through an electromagnet. The current keeps changing direction.

② The permanent magnet repels and attracts the electromagnet. This turns the shaft of the motor.

③ As the shaft of the motor turns, electrical energy changes to energy of motion.

4. Circle the electromagnet in each illustration on this page.

I Wonder . . . Why does a motor require electric current to produce motion?

_____

_____

_____

_____

_____

_____

5. Sequence the steps in getting electricity from the generator to your home.

a. Energy from _____ or _____ turns the generators that produce the electricity.

↓

b. Power lines carry _____ to customers.

↓

c. The _____ is used in homes and businesses.

Generating Electricity

You have learned that an electric motor uses magnetism to change electrical energy into energy of motion. A generator does the opposite of an electric motor. A **generator** (JEHN uh ray tuhr) uses magnetism to change energy of motion into electrical energy.

From Generator to Customer

ENERGY SOURCE Energy from falling water or burning fuel helps generators produce electricity.

ELECTRIC POWER LINES Power lines carry electricity to customers.

Giant generators produce the electricity that lights up whole cities and runs machines. These generators have permanent magnets with lots of power. They have huge loops of wire. The loops move across the magnetic field of the permanent magnet. This produces electric current in the wires.

Energy in motion moves the wire loops of a generator. This energy can come from such things as burning coal, steam, falling water, or wind.

HOMES AND BUSINESSES
Electricity is used every day.

6. Compare and contrast motors and generators.

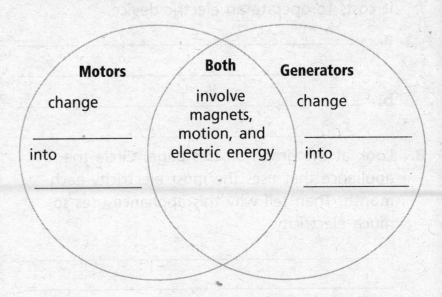

Motors	Both	Generators
change _____ into _____	involve magnets, motion, and electric energy	change _____ into _____

I Wonder . . . Why do power plants use huge generators with many coils of wire?

_____

_____

7. List the two factors that determine how much it costs to operate an electric device.

a. _____

_____

b. _____

_____

8. Look at the graph on this page. Circle the appliance that uses the most electricity each month. Then tell why this appliance uses so much electricity.

_____

_____

The Cost of Using Electricity

Using electricity costs money. You pay for how much electricity you use. Each month, you get an electric bill for the total amount of electricity you have used in your home.

The cost of using an electric machine depends on two things. One is the amount of time it is used. The other is the amount of electrical energy it needs to run.

Some machines use electricity only part of the time. Examples are fans and washing machines. Other machines use electricity 24 hours a day, every day. Examples are refrigerators and clocks. The graph shows the average monthly cost of using some everyday machines.

A fan only uses electricity when it is turned on.

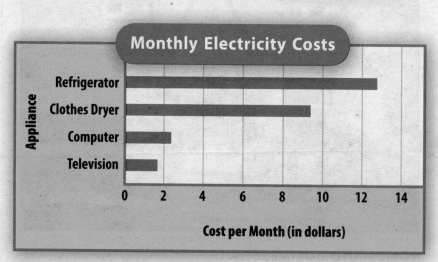

Monthly Electricity Costs

Appliance | Cost per Month (in dollars)
Refrigerator
Clothes Dryer
Computer
Television

0 2 4 6 8 10 12 14

Which of these uses the most electricity each month?

A computer still uses electricity when it is resting or turned off.

Some electric machines use electricity even when you are not using them! If a computer were left on "sleep" for an entire year, it would still use about $40 worth of electricity.

Some things have built-in clocks. The clocks run on electricity even if the machine is turned off. Look at your radio, DVD player, or stereo. Do they have a clock that is on all the time, even if you are not using the machine? This use of electricity costs money. Follow these tips to save electricity:

- Use a safety cord to plug in TVs, DVD players, and other machines. When the switch is turned off, no electricity reaches the machines.
- Turn your computer off instead of letting it sleep.
- Turn off lights, TVs, and stereos when you are not in the room.

COMPARE AND CONTRAST

How do a refrigerator and a washing machine differ in their use of electricity?

Summary Electricity can produce magnetism, and magnetism can produce electricity. Together, magnetism and electricity can produce energy of motion. List two ways that you can save electricity.

a. _____
   _____

b. _____
   _____

▶ **Compare and Contrast** How do a refrigerator and a washing machine differ in their use of electricity?

Refrigerator
uses electricity
_____

Both
Both use electricity

Washing machine
uses electricity
_____

Write a sentence telling how *electric currents* and *electric circuits* are related.

_____

_____

_____

conductors (kuhn DUHK tuhrz) Materials that negatively charged particles can move through easily.

electric cell (ih LEHK trihk sehl) A device that turns chemical energy into electrical energy.

electric charges (ih LEHK trihk CHAHRJ ehs) Tiny particles that carry units of electricity.

electric circuit (ih LEHK trihk SUR kiht) The pathway that an electric current follows.

electric current (ih LEHK trihk KUR uhnt) A continuous flow of electric charges.

electromagnet (ih lehk troh MAG niht) A strong temporary magnet that uses electricity to produce magnetism.

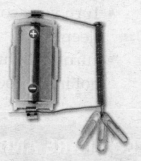

generator (JEHN uh ray tuhr) A devise that uses magnetism to convert energy of motion into electrical energy.

Glossary

insulators (IHN suh lay tuhrz) Materials that electric charges do not flow through easily.

magnet (MAG niht) An object that attracts certain metals, mainly iron.

magnetic poles (mag NEHT ihk pohlz) The two areas on a magnet with the greatest magnetic force.

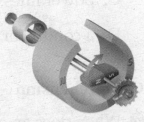

motor (MOH tur) A device that changes electrical energy into energy of motion.

parallel circuit (PAIR uh lehl SUR kiht) A circuit in which the parts are connected so that the electric current passes along more than one pathway.

series circuit (SIHR eez SUR kiht) A circuit in which the parts are connected so that the electric current passes through each part along a single pathway.

static electricity (STAT ihk ih lehk TRIHS ih tee) An electric charge that builds up on a material.

 Visit www.eduplace.com to play word games and puzzles.

Complete the word web about types of electric circuits.

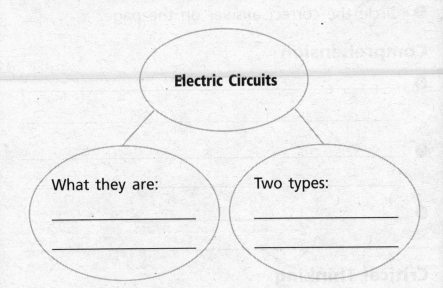

Electric Circuits

What they are:

_____

_____

Two types:

_____

_____

161

Chapter Review

KWL

WHAT DID YOU LEARN?

GPS CRCT Prep

❶ (Circle) the correct answer on the page.

Comprehension

❷ _____
_____

❸ _____
_____

❹ _____
_____

Critical Thinking

❺ _____
_____
_____
_____

Think About What You Have Read

GPS CRCT Prep

❶ A constant flow of electric charges is called

   A. magnetism.

   B. electric current.

   C. power lines.

   D. a conductor.

S5P3b

Comprehension

❷ When does an object have an overall positive charge?

❸ Explain why a switch might be added to a circuit. Give examples.

❹ Why don't magnets attract wooden objects?

Critical Thinking

❺ You reach for a doorknob and get a small shock. Use what you know about static electricity to explain why this happened.

Classifying Organisms

KWL

WHAT DO YOU KNOW?

List one fact about each of these topics:

a. Groups of organisms:

_____

_____

_____

b. Plant classification:

_____

_____

_____

c. Animal classification:

_____

_____

_____

Contents

WHAT DO YOU WANT TO KNOW?

Skim the pictures and headings in this chapter. List one thing you want to find out about each of these topics:

a. Types of bacteria:

_____

_____

_____

b. Angiosperms:

_____

_____

_____

c. Types of vertebrates:

_____

_____

_____

_____

VOCABULARY

bacteria Small, single-celled organisms that do not have a nucleus. *(noun)*

dichotomous key A tool used to identify organisms based on contrasting pairs of characteristics. *(noun)*

fungi A kingdom of organisms, with a nucleus, that get nutrients by decomposing other organisms. *(noun)*

kingdom The highest level of biological classification. *(noun)*

protist A single-celled or multi-cellular organism that may share characteristics with plants, fungi, and animals. *(noun)*

protozoa Animal-like protists, including amoebas and paramecium. *(noun)*

VOCABULARY SKILL: Word Origins

The word *dichotomous* comes from the Greek word *dicha*, which means "in two." How does the original word connect with the vocabulary term?

_____

_____

S5L3a. Use magnifiers such as microscopes or hand lens to observe cells and their structure.

1 How Do Scientists Classify Organisms?

Scientists use a biological classification system to show how groups of living things, known as organisms, relate to one another.

The Six Kingdoms

Earth is home to millions of different species. A species is a specific kind of living thing. To keep track of them all, scientists use a system of biological classification. This system is a way to put species into groups.

The largest group in this system is called a **kingdom**. Many scientists use six kingdoms. Bacteria have two kingdoms. Protists, fungi, plants, and animals each have one kingdom.

To group organisms, scientists study the internal and external structures of living things. They also study individual cells and the chemical processes inside cells. Scientists then use this information to group species according to how closely related they are.

The impala and the kudu are animals that live on the plains of Africa. They are the same in some ways and are different in other ways.

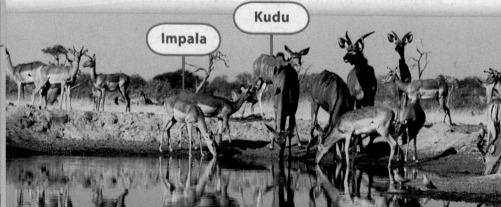

Kudu

Impala

Classifying Tools

One night you see a flying animal. Is it a bird? Then you see it has fur. Do birds have fur? No, so it cannot be a bird. You see that the wings look like thin skin stretched over bone.

What animal can fly, has fur, and has wings like skin? It must be a bat. The answer to each question helped you determine what the animal is. Each answer also helped you determine what the animal could not be.

This process is similar to how scientists identify living things. They use a tool called a **dichotomous** (dy KAHT uh muhs) **key**. The word *dichotomous* means "divided into two parts." The key gives two characteristics to choose between. Each choice leads to another pair of characteristics. These choices help scientists determine what the organism can be.

Classifying Most Living Things

Follow this key to classify most of Earth's living things.

1. List four things that scientists study in order to classify organisms into kingdoms and their subgroups.

a. _____

b. _____

c. _____

d. _____

2. Use your finger to trace the path that classifies fungi. Circle the correct answers.

Single-celled?   YES   NO

Makes its own food?   YES   NO

Eats food?   YES   NO

Circle the correct answer.

3. Which of these tools is most useful for studying bacteria?

   A. telescope

   B. microscope

   C. binoculars

   D. two-pan balance

S5L3a

4. What makes bacteria cells different from the cells of all other organisms?

_____

_____

I Wonder . . . Why do you think it is important to wash your hands before you eat?

_____

_____

_____

_____

Bacteria

Bacteria are small organisms with a single cell. The cell does not have a nucleus. This makes bacteria different from other living things. Bacteria are some of the smallest living things. They can only be seen with a microscope. If you put 10,000 bacteria in a line, the line would not even stretch across your fingernail.

There are more bacteria than any other organism. They live almost everywhere on Earth. They live in soil, in water, and inside other organisms. Bacteria can even live in ice or rock! Some kinds of bacteria are useful. Bacteria in your stomach help you digest food. Other types of bacteria can cause disease. Strep throat is caused by harmful bacteria.

Bacteria (Two Kingdoms)

- Bacteria have a single cell.
- A bacterial cell does not have a nucleus.
- Bacteria are the most numerous kind of organism.

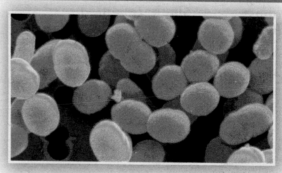

Cocci bacteria like these are found in foods such as pickles. The bacteria produce an acid. The acid gives pickles part of the flavor and helps preserve them.

Bacteria are separated into two kingdoms. These kingdoms are archaebacteria and eubacteria. Archaebacteria (AHR kee bak TIHR ee uh) means "ancient bacteria." These bacteria have lived on Earth longer than any other organism. Today they live under conditions that would kill other living things. Some kinds live only where there is no oxygen. Other kinds live in areas where the heat is too high to allow most forms of life to live.

Eubacteria (YOO bak TIHR ee uh) cannot live in such harsh conditions. Most bacteria are eubacteria. Eubacteria cells have a variety of ways to get food. Some kinds of eubacteria use the Sun's energy to make food. Other kinds get their food from eating non-living and living materials.

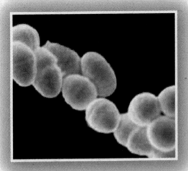

Cocci are round bacteria that sometimes join together in clusters or long chains.

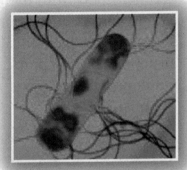

Bacilli are rod-shaped bacteria and are common in soil and water.

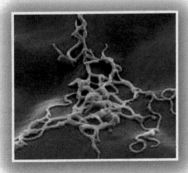

Spirochetes look and wriggle like worms.

5. List the two kingdoms of bacteria. Write a description of each kingdom.

a. _____
_____
_____

b. _____
_____
_____

6. Describe the shape of each type of bacteria. Draw each type.

a. cocci: _____

b. bacilli: _____

c. spirochetes: _____

169

7. Contrast bacteria and protists.

Characteristic	Bacteria	Protists
Number of cells?	Always one cell	
Nucleus?	no	

8. Read paragraph 2. Circle the ways protozoa move through their environment.

9. Fill in the blanks to describe where protozoa live.

Protozoa live wherever there is _____.

They also can be found in _____ and inside _____.

Protists

A **protist** is an organism that may have some characteristics of fungi, plants, and animals. The organisms in Kingdom Protista are very different. Some protists have more than one cell, but most have just a single cell. Each protist cell has a nucleus. The cells of protists also have special structures that do certain things for the cell, such as changing food into energy.

Animal-like protists are called **protozoa** (PROH tuh zoh uh). Protozoa cannot make their own food. They get their food from their surroundings. Most protozoa can move through their environment. Some seem to slip and slide like jelly. Others use moving tail-like structures or fine hairs. Protozoa live wherever there is water and can also be found in moist soil and inside organisms.

Protist Kingdom

- Protists may have a single cell or many cells.
- Protist cells have a nucleus, and their structures have two or more parts.
- Some protists have the same characteristics as fungi, plants, or animals.

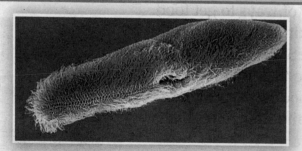

A paramecium moves using tiny, hair-like structures called cilia. These cilia cover most of the paramecium's body. The cilia work like oars to move the paramecium forward and backward.

Algae are plant-like protists. These protists use energy from the Sun to make their own food. Like plants, they produce oxygen, so they play an important role in nature. Many other organisms depend on them for food and oxygen. Some plant-like protists can be seen only with a microscope. Others grow to be as tall as trees.

Perhaps the most interesting kinds of protists are those that have characteristics of fungi. They get their food from their surroundings. Some reproduce through spores, as fungi do. Yet many can move from place to place, although they move very slowly.

Fungus-like protists can have a big effect on humans and animals. They attack vegetable and fruit crops, such as corn and grapes. They also attack animals, such as fish.

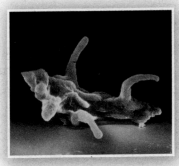
Amoebas (uh MEE buhz) use a "false foot" to move.

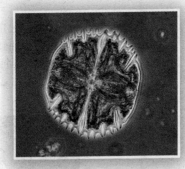
Algae (AL jee) are plant-like protists. Algae make much of the oxygen in Earth's atmosphere.

Slime mold is a fungus-like protist. Some kinds ooze slowly over dead trees.

10. Complete the chart about the three types of protists.

Protists			
Type of Protist	Animal-like	Plant-like	Fungus-like
Example			
How it gets energy			

11. How can fungus-like protists affect humans and other animals?

_____

_____

12. Read paragraph 1 about fungi. (Circle) the number of fungi species that scientists have identified.

13. Circle YES or NO to describe the characteristics of fungi.

a. cells have a nucleus?   YES   NO

b. make own food?   YES   NO

c. reproduce through spores?   YES   NO

d. all are safe to eat?   YES   NO

Fungi

Organisms in Kingdom **Fungi** (FUHN jee) can be small, one-celled organisms. They can also grow to large masses as wide as 30 cm (1 ft) or more. Scientists have identified over 70,000 species of fungi.

Like all other kingdoms except bacteria, fungi cells have nuclei. Their cell walls are made of the same substance as the hard shells of insects.

Fungi Kingdom

- Fungi cells have a nucleus. Their structures have two or more parts.
- Fungi absorb their food and break down other organisms.
- Fungi grow fast and reproduce through spores.

You can eat some species of mushrooms. Others are poisonous. Only an expert should pick wild mushrooms.

Mushroom Life Cycle

1 A mushroom with a stalk and cap is the above-ground part of certain fungi species.

2 Spores are released from the mushroom cap.

3 Spores grow on a surface and form the mycelium.

4 The mycelium produces mature, or fully grown, mushrooms.

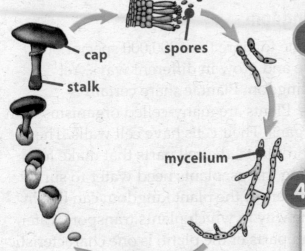

cap

stalk

spores

mycelium

Fungi do not make or eat food. Instead, fungi absorb nutrients from their environment. They decompose, or break down, the tissues of other organisms. Fungi cannot move from place to place. Yet they can grow very quickly over a surface. Their spores can travel very far in wind or water.

CLASSIFY

What are the six kingdoms of living things?

Summary Biological classification systems show how living things are related to each other. How do the life processes of fungi help plants?

_____

_____

_____

▶ Classify What are the six kingdoms of living things?

Six Kingdoms

_____

_____

_____

_____

_____

173

VOCABULARY

angiosperm A vascular plant that produces seeds from flowers. *(noun)*

gymnosperm A vascular plant that produces seeds, but not flowers or fruits. *(noun)*

nonvascular Lacking a water-transport system. *(adjective)*

vascular Having a tube-like water-transport system. *(adjective)*

VOCABULARY SKILL: Prefixes

The word *nonvascular* has the prefix *non*, which means "not." Use the meaning of the prefix and the definition for *vascular* given above to write a definition for *nonvascular*.

_____

_____

_____

GPS **S5L1b.** Demonstrate how plants are sorted into groups.

2 How Are Plants Classified?

All plants have more than one cell. Almost all plants make their own food using the Sun's energy. Plants are classified according to the ways they transport water and reproduce.

The Plant Kingdom

Earth is home to more than 300,000 species of plants that live and grow in different ways. Yet members of Kingdom Plantae share certain characteristics. Plants are many-celled organisms with tissues and organs. Their cells have cell walls. The cells have chloroplasts, the cell parts that make food.

Like all living things, plants need water to survive. Yet many members of the plant kingdom can live in dry places. The way in which plants transport water, or carry it to all parts of the plant, is one characteristic that scientists use to put plants into groups.

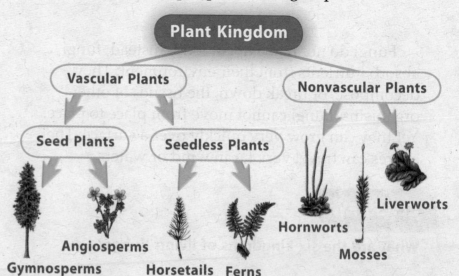

Plant Kingdom

Vascular Plants — Nonvascular Plants

Seed Plants — Seedless Plants

Gymnosperms — Angiosperms — Horsetails — Ferns — Hornworts — Mosses — Liverworts

Nonvascular (nahn VAS kyoo luhr) plants absorb water. Water slowly passes directly from cell to cell. Because nonvascular plants do not have tissues to transport water, they must live close to a water source. The lack of a water transport system keeps nonvascular plants from growing very tall. Many barely reach a few inches tall when they are fully grown.

Vascular plants have tissues that act like tubes. These tube-like tissues transport water and nutrients taken up from soil through the plant's roots. This means that vascular plants do not have to live close to a body of water. The vascular system provides support and allows plants to grow very tall. Over time, vascular plants have developed ways of living in most climates, dry and wet.

Plant Kingdom

- Plants have many cells.
- Plants have tissues and organs.
- Plants have cell walls and chloroplasts.
- Plants make their own food.

Sugar maple trees produce a sweet sap. In late winter and early spring, people cut small holes in the tree bark to collect the sap. The sap is used to make maple syrup.

1. List four characteristics that all plants share.

   a. _____

   b. _____

   c. _____

   d. _____

2. Look at the dichotomous key of the plant kingdom. Use the key to identify the characteristics of ferns.

   Vascular or nonvascular? _____

   Seed plant or seedless plant? _____

3. List two benefits of a vascular system to land-dwelling plants.

   a. _____

   b. _____

4. Complete the chart to describe the characteristics of ferns.

Ferns	
Characteristic	**YES or NO?**
Have vascular tissue?	
Have seeds?	
Make spores?	

5. Use your finger to trace the life cycle of a gymnosperm. Read the description of each step. What is a key difference between ferns and gymnosperms?

_____

_____

Ferns

One common type of vascular plant is the fern. Ferns have roots, stems, and leaves. Each of these parts contains vascular tissue. Ferns do not have seeds. To reproduce, seedless vascular plants make spores. A spore holds only half the beginning of a complete new plant inside it. A spore falls off a plant and germinates. A male plant must fertilize a female plant to produce a new fern.

Gymnosperms

A **gymnosperm** (JIHM noh spurm) is a vascular plant that produces seeds. The seeds rest in berries or on woody structures called cones. Seeds contain plant embryos, the beginnings of new plants. The seed provides protection and a source of food for the embryo. Seeds can travel long distances, allowing plants to spread to new areas.

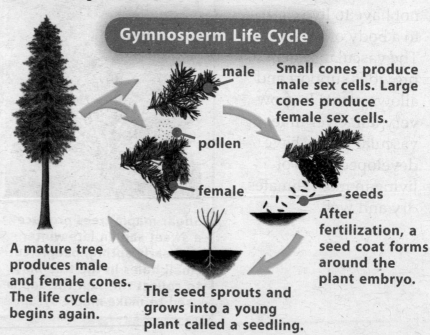

Gymnosperm Life Cycle

Small cones produce male sex cells. Large cones produce female sex cells.

male

pollen

female

seeds

After fertilization, a seed coat forms around the plant embryo.

A mature tree produces male and female cones. The life cycle begins again.

The seed sprouts and grows into a young plant called a seedling.

Conifer

Cycad

Ginkgo

Gnetophyte

GYMNOSPERMS These plants are all types of gymnosperms. They produce seeds but do not produce flowers or fruit.

There are four main groups of gymnosperms: conifers, cycads (SY kads), ginkgos, and gnetophytes (NEE toh fyts). Many conifers are pine trees. Most conifers are called evergreens because they keep their needle-like leaves all year long. Conifers are important in our daily lives. Most paper is made from conifer wood fibers.

Cycads look like palm trees and live mainly in tropical areas. Cycads produce cones instead of flowers. In some places, cycad seeds and trunks are used for food.

Ginkgos are attractive trees that resist many diseases and air pollution. Unlike other gymnosperms, ginkgo trees lose their leaves every year.

Gnetophytes are found in both very wet and very dry environments. Some species have unusual leather-like leaves that grow on vines. Other species resemble shrubs.

6. List four main groups of gymnosperms and describe each one.

a. _____

_____

b. _____

_____

c. _____

_____

d. _____

_____

Circle the correct answer.

7. **Unlike plants in other groups, gymnosperms produce**

   A. fruits and flowers.

   B. seeds in cones.

   C. roots and stems.

   D. tall, woody plants.

   S5L1b

I Wonder . . . Flowers that depend on animals to carry pollen often are very colorful. Why do you think this is so?

_____

_____

_____

Angiosperms

When you think of a flower, what image comes into your head? Do you think of a daisy or a rose? People usually notice a flower's beautiful colors and smell. For plants, flowers are necessary for reproduction.

An **angiosperm** is a vascular plant that produces flowers. The flowers make seeds and fruits to protect seeds. Some flowers have both male and female organs within one flower. Other flowers may have either male or female sex organs.

Like gymnosperms, angiosperms produce pollen. Bees often help angiosperms spread pollen from one flower to another. Pollen from a flower sticks to the bee's legs. When the bee visits a new flower, pollen falls off the bee. If the new flower has female sex organs, the pollen fertilizes the flower.

Angiosperms			
	Plant	**Flower**	**Seed/Fruit**
Corn			
Apple			

FLOWERS All flowers produce seeds, but flowers differ in many ways among plant species.

Fruiting Plant Life Cycle

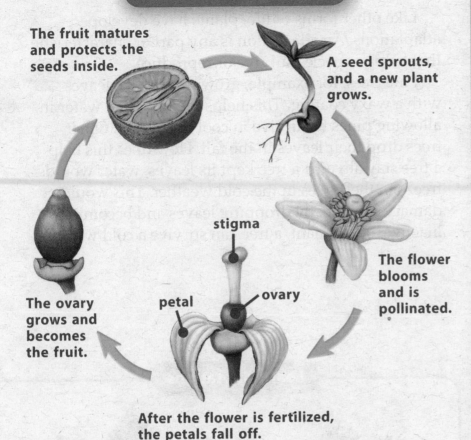

The fruit matures and protects the seeds inside.

A seed sprouts, and a new plant grows.

The flower blooms and is pollinated.

After the flower is fertilized, the petals fall off.

The ovary grows and becomes the fruit.

stigma

petal

ovary

When you think of a fruit, you may think of the apple or orange you had at lunch. Did you know that an avocado and coconut are also fruits? So are tomatoes, dates, and many other foods.

Scientists define a fruit as the plant part that contains the plant's fertilized seeds. All plants that produce flowers also produce fruit. You can eat many fruits, but not all fruits can be eaten. A cotton boll used to make cotton fabric is a fruit. The spinning seedpods that fall from certain trees in autumn are, too. Of course, you would not want to eat these fruits.

8. Study the diagram of the fruiting plant life cycle. Then describe each stage.

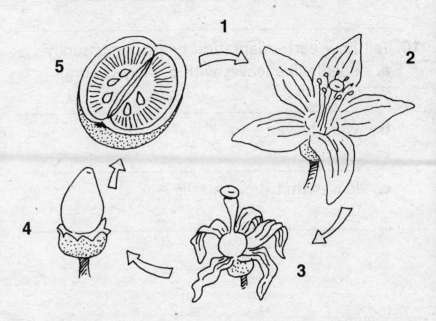

1

2

3

4

5

Step 1: A seed sprouts and a new plant grows.

Step 2: _____
_____

Step 3: _____
_____

Step 4: _____
_____

Step 5: _____
_____

179

9. What is an adaptation?

_____

_____

10. Tell how each adaptation helps plants survive.

a. needle-like leaves with a waxy coating:

_____

b. wide leaves:

_____

c. leaves that drop in fall:

_____

Plant Adaptations

Like other forms of life, plants have developed adaptations. An adaptation is any part or characteristic that helps a species survive or reproduce.

Pine trees, for example, grow needle-like leaves with a waxy coating. This helps the tree keep water in, allowing pines to survive in cool dry places. Other trees drop their leaves in the fall. How does this help a tree stay alive? If a tree kept its leaves, water would freeze in the leaves in the cold weather. This would damage the tree. By dropping leaves and becoming inactive, or dormant, a tree can survive a cold winter.

Leaf Adaptations

Spruce trees have needle-like leaves that help them keep water in.

Many trees have wide leaves to gather more sunlight.

Cactus plants are adapted to hot, dry climates. They have thick stems to hold water in. A waxy coating keeps the cactus from drying out. The spines keep desert animals from stealing the water or eating the plant. These spines are actually the plant's leaves. These are adapted for the desert climate.

Plants' life cycles are also examples of adaptations. Some plants, called annuals, usually complete their life cycle in a single year. Other plants, called biennials, live for two years. Plants called perennials grow back every year.

COMPARE AND CONTRAST

How do vascular and nonvascular plants differ?

Cactus spines are its leaves, adapted to protect the plant.

Summary All plants are multicellular. Almost all make their own food by using the Sun's energy. Plants are classified according to the ways they transport water and reproduce.

How are perennials, biennials, and annuals different?

_____

_____

 Compare and Contrast How do vascular and nonvascular plants differ?

Vascular	Nonvascular
tube-like tissues that transport water	

181

VOCABULARY

amphibian A vertebrate that begins its life in water but lives part of the time on land. *(noun)*

cnidarian Invertebrate with radial symmetry, a saclike body, a true mouth, and the ability to digest food. *(noun)*

invertebrate An animal without a backbone. *(noun)*

symmetry Matching form on opposite sides of a dividing line. *(noun)*

vertebrate An animal with a backbone. *(noun)*

VOCABULARY SKILL: Using pictures

Read the definition of *symmetry.* Then look at the pictures of two types of symmetry shown on this page. Which type of symmetry do you think humans have? Explain.

_____

_____

_____

S5L1a. Demonstrate how animals are sorted into groups (vertebrate and invertebrate) and how vertebrates are sorted into groups (fish, amphibian, reptile, bird, and mammal).

182

3 How Are Animals Classified?

The differences between animals determine how they are classified.

The Animal Kingdom

The Kingdom Animalia includes an amazing variety of life. Some of these animals swim. Some fly. Many walk. Some do all of these things. There are animals that you can see only with a microscope. Others are as tall as a house. Humans belong to the animal kingdom. There are several characteristics that people share with all animals.

Animals also have some of the same characteristics as organisms from other kingdoms. Like plants, animals have many cells. However, animals do not take in energy from the Sun as plants do. Animals take in food from their environment by eating. They break down and digest food for its energy and nutrients.

radial symmetry

bilateral symmetry

Animals with bilateral symmetry have bodies with two similar halves, like dogs.

Animals with radial symmetry have body parts arranged equally around a middle point, like starfish.

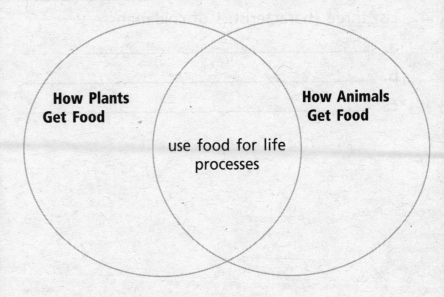

Animal Kingdom

- Animals have many cells.
- Animals need oxygen.
- Animals eat food.
- Most animals move from place to place.
- Most animals reproduce sexually.

Meerkats live in the Kalahari Desert in Africa. They live in family groups. All members of the group take care of their young. All members of the family also watch out for predators and help find food for the group.

Characteristics of Animals

Biologists study many characteristics to classify animals. These are the most common:

- Animals have many cells.
- Animals have specialized cells that form tissues and organs.
- Animals need oxygen to breathe.
- Animals consume other organisms to get the nutrients and energy they need.
- Most animals are able to move at some point in their lives.
- Most animals reproduce sexually.

First an organism is identified as an animal. Then it is classified again into phylum, class, order, family, genus, and species.

1. Compare and contrast how plants and animals get food.

How Plants Get Food

use food for life processes

How Animals Get Food

2. List the six most common characteristics of animals.

a. _____

b. _____

c. _____

d. _____

e. _____

f. _____

183

3. What is an invertebrate?

_____

4. List three characteristics of cnidarians.

a. _____

b. _____

c. _____

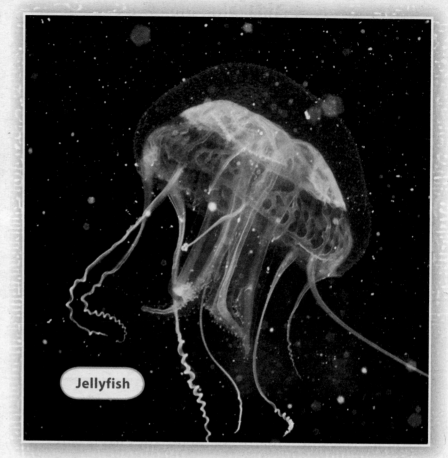

Jellyfish

CNIDARIANS Jellyfish and coral are cnidarians (ny DAIR ee uhns). They have mouths and simple digestive systems. They have radial symmetry. Their parts repeat around a center.

Invertebrates

An animal without a backbone is called an **invertebrate** (ihn VUR tuh briht). Invertebrates are very different and include the largest number of animal species. Invertebrates have different kinds of body symmetries. **Symmetry** is a matching pattern, either on opposite sides of an imaginary dividing line or around a middle point.

ECHINODERMS Starfish, sea urchins, and sea cucumbers are echinoderms, a name that means "spiny skin." They often use sucker-like parts to catch prey.

Sea Cucumber

Sponges are very simple animals. They lack tissues, organs, and true body symmetry. Most sponges live in oceans. Some live in fresh water. Sponges filter bits of food from water that passes through them.

Sponges

5. List three kinds of echinoderms.

   a. _____

   b. _____

   c. _____

6. What do these three echinoderms have in common?

   _____

   _____

I Wonder . . . Some sponges live attached to the shells of hermit crabs. How might this benefit both animals?

   _____

   _____

   _____

   _____

   _____

   _____

7. List four groups of arthropods.

a. _____

b. _____

c. _____

d. _____

8. Complete the sentences to describe characteristics of arthropods.

a. Have body parts with _____.

b. Parts surrounded by a hard covering called

an _____.

c. Have _____ symmetry.

Lobster

Scorpion

ARTHROPODS Lobsters, crabs, spiders, and insects are all types of arthropods. This animal group has the most species. Arthropods have body parts with movable joints. Their parts are surrounded by a hard covering called an exoskeleton. They have bilateral symmetry. This means the left and right halves of their bodies are similar.

Snail

Squid

MOLLUSKS Clams and oysters are mollusks. So are snails, squids, and octopuses. Mollusks have soft bodies. Most mollusks have shells. They live, eat, and move in many different ways. Adult clams do not move. Snails move very slowly. Squids and octopuses are some of the fastest creatures in the water.

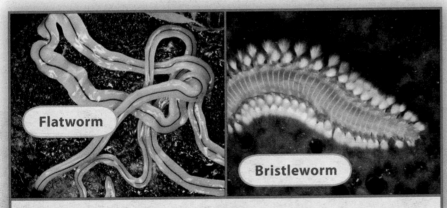

Flatworm

Bristleworm

WORMS Different groups of worms include flatworms and roundworms. Another group includes earthworms. All worms have bilateral symmetry. You can tell where their heads are. Worms have simple organ systems. Some worms are parasites. They live and feed off the body of another organism, or host.

9. Order these three types of mollusks from slowest mover to fastest mover. Number the slowest mover 1. Number the fastest mover 3.

snail   octopus   adult clam

_____   _____   _____

10. What two features do all worms have in common?

a. _____

b. _____

I Wonder . . . Some worms, such as earthworms, have long, round bodies. Why aren't they described as having radial symmetry instead of bilateral symmetry?

_____

_____

_____

_____

_____

11. The body temperature of cold-blooded animals depends on the temperature of the environment outside their bodies. (Circle) a cold-blooded vertebrate shown on this page.

12. How do fish breathe?

_____

_____

Cold-blooded Vertebrates

An animal that has a backbone is called a **vertebrate** (VUR tuh briht). A backbone is a series of bones joined together with a flexible material called cartilage. Vertebrates may be warm-blooded or cold-blooded. These terms do not refer to the actual temperature of the animal's blood. The terms refer to how the animal maintains its body temperature.

Fish Fish represent a great number of species among vertebrates. Most fish have a bony skeleton. Others, such as sharks, have a skeleton that is only cartilage. Even though there is a great variety of fish, they all share important characteristics.

Fish have gills that allow them to breathe in water. The gills take oxygen from the water.

Most fish are cold-blooded and have a very good sense of smell.

FISH Most fish have sleek bodies that allow them to swim easily.

AMPHIBIANS More than 350 species of salamanders have been identified. Frogs and toads are also amphibians.

Amphibians Frogs and toads are amphibians. An **amphibian** (am FIHB ee uhn) usually needs to live close to water but does not spend its entire life in it. Some have lungs that allow them to breathe outside of water. Some don't have lungs at all. These amphibians use their skin to exchange gases with the air.

Amphibians need water to reproduce. Most species have eggs that would dry out on land, so they must lay their eggs in water or moist places. Many begin their early lives in water.

Salamanders and newts are amphibians with tails. Like frogs, they have smooth, moist skin. Most of these animals live in moist areas where they can easily get to water. There are some, though, that live close to deserts.

13. Fill in the web to give examples of different types of amphibians.

```
                  ┌─────────────────┐
                  │   Amphibians    │
                  └─────────────────┘
                   /               \
┌──────────────────────┐   ┌──────────────────────┐
│ Adults have no tails │   │ Adults have tails    │
│                      │   │                      │
│ a. _____  │   │ a. _____  │
│                      │   │                      │
│ b. _____  │   │ b. _____  │
└──────────────────────┘   └──────────────────────┘
```

14. Give one reason why amphibians live close to water or in moist places all of their lives.

_____

_____

15. List three examples of reptiles.

a. _____

b. _____

c. _____

16. Compare and contrast reptile and amphibian eggs.

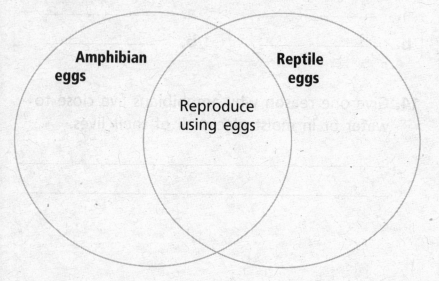

Amphibian eggs | Reptile eggs

Reproduce using eggs

REPTILES Almost 8,000 species of reptiles are known. Scientists discover about 60 more each year.

Reptiles Reptiles are cold-blooded animals. Some reptiles, however, are very good at keeping their inside body temperature steady. All reptiles have tough, dry outer skin. The flexible, scaly skin of reptiles is a waterproof coating. Their skin helps them keep water in their bodies.

Many reptiles live near water and spend time in it, but they reproduce on land. Most reptiles lay eggs. Reptile eggs have a tough outer covering that prevents them from easily drying out.

Snakes are reptiles. So are turtles, tortoises, lizards, crocodiles, and alligators. Snakes rely on their sense of smell and their tongues to know what is going on around them. When a snake flicks its tongue, it is sampling the air or the soil.

Warm-blooded Vertebrates

Birds and mammals are warm-blooded animals. Their inside body temperature stays about the same all the time. Their body cells produce enough heat to keep their bodies warm even when the temperature outside their bodies is very low.

Birds Different bird species have adapted to live almost anywhere in the world. Birds are the only animal group that has feathers. For most birds, the feathers on their wings help them to fly.

Birds have beaks instead of teeth. Some birds eat mammals, fish, and other birds. These are birds of prey, such as eagles, falcons, and owls. Birds of prey have sharp, hooked beaks. Birds like woodpeckers have long, thin beaks that allow them to dig into tree bark for their favorite food, insects.

All birds have feathers and wings, but not all birds can fly. Ostriches can run as fast as 70 km per hour!

Water birds usually use webbed feet to paddle water. Ducks, geese, and other plant-eaters have flat beaks, or bills. These help them pick up slippery food.

GPS CRCT Prep

Circle the correct answer.

17. **Which of the following is characteristic of birds and mammals *only*?**

   A. They lay eggs.

   B. They have a backbone.

   C. They have radial symmetry.

   D. They are warm-blooded.

   S5L1a

18. What feature is unique to birds among all the animal groups?

_____

_____

I Wonder . . . Birds are found in all types of environments. Why do you think that this is so?

_____

_____

_____

19. Circle the characteristics that apply to mammals.

Feathers	Hair
Lay eggs	Give birth to live young
Teeth	Beaks

20. What can you tell about a mammal from the shape of its teeth?

_____

_____

_____

Mammals Mammals have many different organs and a nervous system that can do many different things. A mammal's brain is fairly large, so mammals can learn and do many things. All mammals have hair at some time in their lives. The hair may be fine or thick and may cover the entire body or only parts of it. Even a whale has whiskers!

Most mammals give birth to live young. All mammals feed milk to their young. Most mammals have teeth. Some have sharp teeth for eating other animals. Others have flat teeth for grinding plants.

Mammals move for many reasons, including to find food or to escape from a predator. They may move on two legs or four. Or, in the case of whales and dolphins, they swim.

Some mammals are herbivores. They eat only plants. Other mammals are carnivores. They eat other animals. Bears are examples of omnivores. They eat plants and animals.

tiger

Classification System

To organize all the species, scientists divide the kingdoms into smaller groups. For example, tigers are members of the animal kingdom. Like many animals, tigers are members of the phylum Chordata. The phylum is the next level after kingdom.

A group called a class comes next. Classes of chordates include Reptilia, Amphibia, and Mammalia.

The next group is called order. The food a mammal eats helps determine its order. Tigers are grouped with cats, dogs, skunks, and other animals in the order Carnivora.

Family and genus are the next levels. Animals in the same genus share many characteristics. Tigers belong to the same family and genus as lions.

The most specific group is the species. Organisms of the same species are able to breed with each other. Tigers belong to the species *Panthera tigris*.

The chart on the next page shows these levels for tigers.

21. Study the chart on page 194 as you read the information on this page. List the levels of animal classification from largest group to smallest group.

a. _____

b. _____

c. _____

d. _____

e. _____

f. _____

g. _____

Summary The differences between animals determine how they are classified. Identify each type of vertebrate shown here.

_____ _____ _____   _____

▶ **Text Structure** To which phylum do tigers belong?

_____

Animal Classification

Kingdom: What organisms have many cells and get energy by consuming food? Answer: Animalia	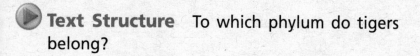
Phylum: What animals have a cord of nerves down their backs? Answer: Chordata	
Class: What chordates have body hair and feed milk to their young? Answer: Mammalia	
Order: What mammals are meat-eating land predators? Answer: Carnivora	
Family: What carnivores have a short muzzle and claws they can pull in? Answer: Felidae	
Genus: What cats are large and live mostly in Africa and Asia? Answer: Panthera	
Species: What cat is the largest and usually has an orange coat with black stripes? Answer: *Panthera tigris*	

TEXT STRUCTURE

To which phylum do tigers belong?

194

amphibian (am FIHB ee uhn), a vertebrate that begins its life in water but lives part of the time on land

angiosperm (AN jee uh spurm), a vascular plant that produces seeds from flowers

archaebacteria (AHR kee bak TIHR ee uh), meaning "ancient bacteria," a kingdom of single-celled living things that resemble eubacteria but typically live in extreme environments

bacteria (bak TIHR ee uh), small, single-celled organisms that do not have a nucleus

cnidarian (ny DAIR ee uhn), invertebrate with radial symmetry, a saclike body, a true mouth, and the ability to digest food

dichotomous key (dy KAHT uh muhs kee), a tool used to identify organisms based on contrasting pairs of characteristics

eubacteria (YOO bak TIHR ee uh), meaning "true bacteria," a kingdom of single-celled living things that lack a nucleus and are found in most every environment

fungi (FUHN jee), a kingdom of organisms, with a nucleus that get nutrients by decomposing other organisms

gymnosperm (JIHM noh spurm), a vascular plant that produces seeds, but not flowers or fruits

Circle the terms that describe the two types of bacteria. Tell how these two types of bacteria are different.

_____

_____

_____

Visit www.eduplace.com/gascp to play word games and puzzles.

Complete the word web to describe two large groups of animals.

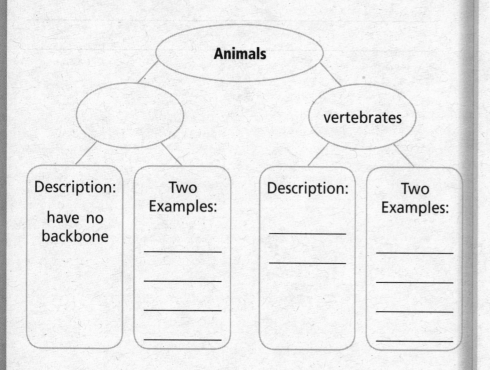

Animals

vertebrates

Description:

have no backbone

Two Examples:

_____

_____

_____

_____

Description:

_____

Two Examples:

_____

_____

_____

_____

196

invertebrate (ihn VUR tuh briht), an animal without a backbone

kingdom (KIHNG duhm), the highest level of biological classification

nonvascular (nahn VAS kyoo luhr), lacking a water-transport system

protist (PROH tihst), a single-celled or multicellular organism that may share characteristics with plants, fungi, and animals

protozoa (PROH tuh zoh uh), animal-like protists, including amoebas and parameciums

symmetry (SIHM ih tree), matching form on opposite sides of a dividing line

vascular (VAS kyoo luhr), having a tube-like water-transport system

vertebrate (VUR tuh briht), an animal with a backbone

Responding

Think About What You Have Read

CRCT Prep

❶ _____ are animal-like protists.

   A. Algae

   B. Mammals

   C. Mosses

   D. Protozoa

Comprehension `S5L4a`

❷ What are two goals of the system used to classify organisms?

❸ What are the two main characteristics scientists use when classifying plants?

❹ Describe the diversity of the animal kingdom.

Critical Thinking

❺ Scientists once classified living things into just two kingdoms: plant and animal. Why do they use six kingdoms today?

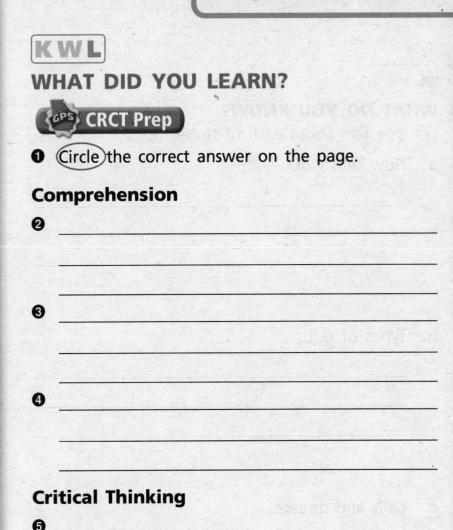

KWL

WHAT DID YOU LEARN?

CRCT Prep

❶ (Circle) the correct answer on the page.

Comprehension

❷ _____

❸ _____

❹ _____

Critical Thinking

❺ _____

WHAT DO YOU KNOW?

List one fact about each of these topics:

a. How cells work:

_____

_____

_____

b. Types of cells:

_____

_____

_____

c. Cells and disease:

_____

_____

_____

Cell Structure and Function

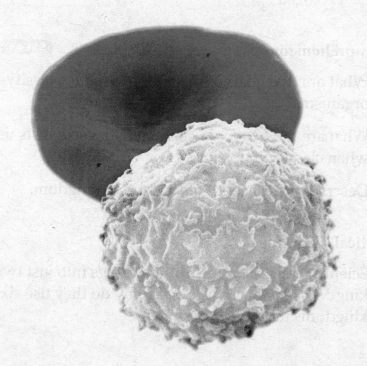

Contents

KWL

WHAT DO YOU WANT TO KNOW?

Skim the pictures and headings in this chapter. List one thing you want to find out about each of these topics:

a. How plant and animal cells differ:

_____

_____

_____

b. How cells work together:

_____

_____

_____

c. How the body fights disease:

_____

_____

_____

chloroplast   An organelle that makes food from sunlight, water, and carbon dioxide. *(noun)*

cytoplasm   The gel-like material that surrounds the internal parts of the cell. *(noun)*

diffusion   Process that spreads substances through a gas or liquid from higher to lower concentration. *(noun)*

nucleus   A part of a cell that directs all cell activities and carries information for cell reproduction. *(noun)*

organelle   A structure that has a specific task within the cell. *(noun)*

osmosis   A type of diffusion that allows water to pass but not the solutes in the water. *(noun)*

VOCABULARY SKILL: Word Parts

The word *chloroplast* is made of two parts. *Chlor-* means "green," and *-plast* means "particle." What can you infer from these meanings about the appearance of a chloroplast?

_____

_____

GPS **S5L3b.** Identify parts of a plant cell (membrane, wall, cytoplasm, nucleus, chloroplasts) and of an animal cell (membrane, cytoplasm, and nucleus) and determine the function of the parts.

200

1 What Do Cells Do?

All living things are made of cells. To stay alive and healthy, cells need food and water. They also need a way to get rid of waste.

Plant Cells and Animal Cells

A single cell is the smallest structure that carries out the activities necessary for life. A cell is like a tiny factory. Different parts of the factory produce or control different things. One part gets food or water. Another part keeps the cell clean. Still other parts are in charge of reproduction. Like parts of a factory, all parts of the cell must work together to run smoothly. An organism cannot survive without cells doing their work.

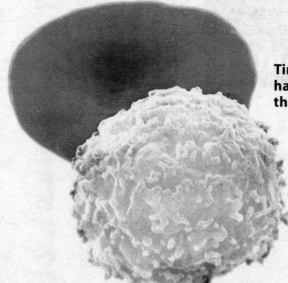

Tiny cells in your body have many smaller parts that work together.

Cell Structures and Their Functions

Cell Structure	Function
Mitochondria	Provide Energy
Vacuoles	Store Materials
Nucleus	Cell Control Center; Reproduction
Cell Membrane	Structure and Transport
Golgi Bodies and Endoplasmic Reticulum	Transport

Each cell structure is like a separate department within a factory. All departments have to do their jobs for the factory to run properly.

All cells have structures that do certain things. Animal cells and plant cells look different, but they share many similar features. They have at least three features in common. Animal and plant cells all have a cell membrane, a nucleus, and cytoplasm.

The cell membrane is the outer covering of the cell. Water and food enter through the cell membrane. Wastes leave through it. Plant cells have an extra structure called the cell wall. The cell wall adds more support to a plant cell.

1. What is a cell?

   _____

   _____

2. List three things that all cells need.

   a. _____

   b. _____

   c. _____

3. List three features that all cells have in common.

   a. _____

   b. _____

   c. _____

Circle the correct answer.

4. **Which cell part is found in plant cells, but not in animal cells?**

   A. cell membrane

   B. nucleus

   C. cell wall

   D. cytoplasm

5. Compare the plant cell on this page with the animal cell on the next page. Circle the names of the parts that appear *only* in plant cells. Then list those parts here.

   a. _____

   b. _____

6. Where is the cytoplasm found?

   _____

   _____

Each animal cell and plant cell has a **nucleus**. The nucleus is the control center for the cell. It carries information for reproduction and directs all cell activities.

The **cytoplasm** (sy tuh PLAZ uhm) is a gel-like material that surrounds all parts of the cell within the membrane. The cytoplasm contains the nucleus and the cell's organelles.

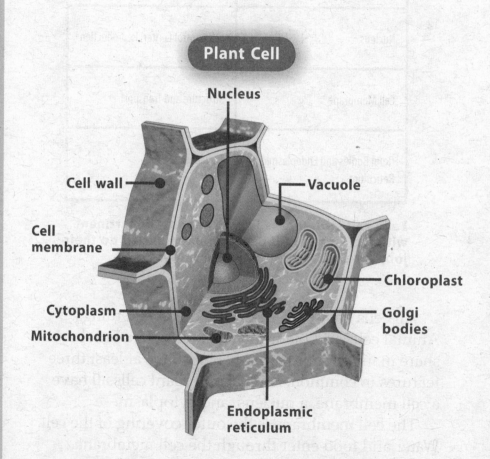

Plant Cell

Nucleus

Cell wall

Vacuole

Cell membrane

Chloroplast

Cytoplasm

Golgi bodies

Mitochondrion

Endoplasmic reticulum

Unlike animal cells, plant cells have a cell wall and chloroplasts. Photosynthesis happens in chloroplasts.

Animal Cell

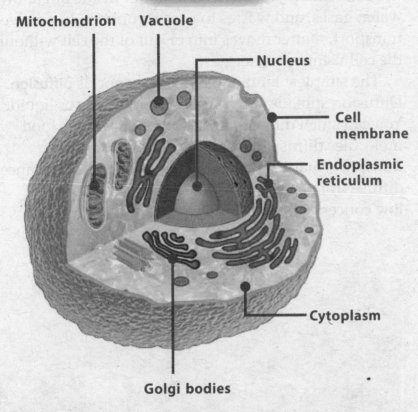

Mitochondrion Vacuole

Nucleus

Cell membrane

Endoplasmic reticulum

Cytoplasm

Golgi bodies

Like plant cells, animal cells have a cell membrane, a nucleus, and cytoplasm.

An **organelle** is a small structure that has a certain job. Look back at the chart on page 201. The chart lists some organelles and their jobs.

Plant cells have a special organelle called a chloroplast. A **chloroplast** uses the energy of sunlight to combine water and carbon dioxide to make food for the cell.

7. Read the clues. Identify which organelle is being described.

Clue	Organelle
the cell's control center	a. _____
provides structure to the cell	b. _____
stores materials	c. _____
transport	d. _____ _____
provides energy	e. _____

I wonder . . . Why don't animal cells have chloroplasts?

_____

_____

_____

_____

203

8. Draw an arrow to show the direction of movement of materials in passive transport.

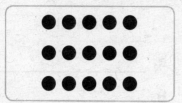 

9. What is diffusion?

_____

_____

_____

Cell Transportation

A cell membrane holds cell matter inside but allows water, gases, and wastes to pass through it. In passive transport, matter moves into or out of the cell without the cell using any energy.

The simplest kind of passive transport is **diffusion**. Diffusion spreads substances through a gas or liquid. You can smell dinner across the room because food molecules diffuse through the air. Diffusion also transports many gases into and out of cells. Substances diffuse from areas of high concentration to areas of low concentration.

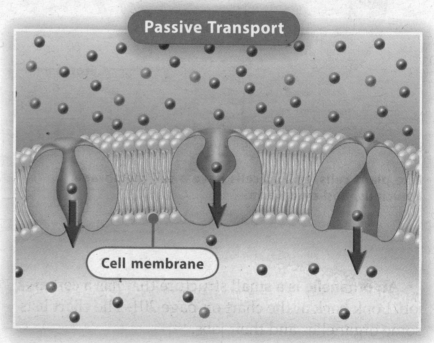

Passive Transport

Cell membrane

Cells use no energy in passive transport. Substances diffuse across the cell membrane. They move from areas of high concentration to low concentration.

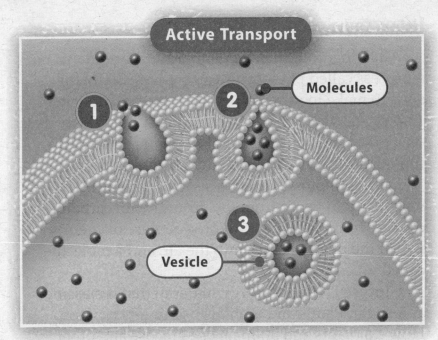

Active Transport

1

2 — Molecules

3

Vesicle

Cells must use energy to move materials across a cell membrane from areas where there is less matter to areas where there is more matter. Cells sometimes form vesicles to do this.

One special form of diffusion is called **osmosis** (ahz MOH sihs). Osmosis is the diffusion of water across a membrane. The membrane often stops many substances that are dissolved in the water. Osmosis often keeps water inside cells.

Sometimes, a cell needs to move materials opposite to the way diffusion would move them. In active transport, substances move from areas with less matter to areas with more matter. The cell must use energy to do this.

Often, large proteins in the cell membrane help move materials in and out. The proteins act as tunnels that allow only certain materials to pass. Scientists study these proteins for clues to how the cell operates.

10. Draw an arrow to show the direction of movement of materials in active transport.

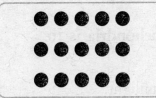

11. What is osmosis?

_____

_____

12. Circle the type of transport that requires energy.

active transport   passive transport

Circle the correct answer.

13. **The function of a mitochondria is to**

    A. store materials.

    B. make energy from sunlight.

    C. break down sugars to release energy.

    D. control movement of materials in and out of the cell.

    S5L3b

14. Tell why glucose is important to both plants and animals.

    _____

    _____

Using Energy

All living things need energy to survive. Plants use a process called photosynthesis (foh toh SIHN thih sihs) to make food by using the energy of sunlight. This process takes place in chloroplasts and depends on a green pigment called chlorophyll (KLAWR uh fihl). Chlorophyll captures energy from sunlight.

During photosynthesis, a series of chemical reactions join water from the ground with carbon dioxide from the air. The byproducts are oxygen, which the plant releases into the air, and a molecule called glucose.

Glucose is a high-energy material that is classified as a sugar. Plants and animals use sugars for food. How do plants and animals use glucose and other sugars? Their cells have organelles called mitochondria. Mitochondria break down sugars so cells can use sugars as energy.

Mitochondria perform cell respiration, the reverse reaction of photosynthesis. This process combines glucose with oxygen to form water and carbon dioxide. A lot of energy is released in the process.

Mitochondria store this energy in a molecule called ATP. This molecule acts like a battery. The cell can draw from ATP whenever it needs to use energy.

Look at the diagram on the next page. The top half shows how structures inside chloroplasts carry out photosynthesis. The bottom half shows cell respiration. In plants and animals, mitochondria perform a process called respiration. In this process, energy from sugars is stored in ATP molecules.

Cells and Energy

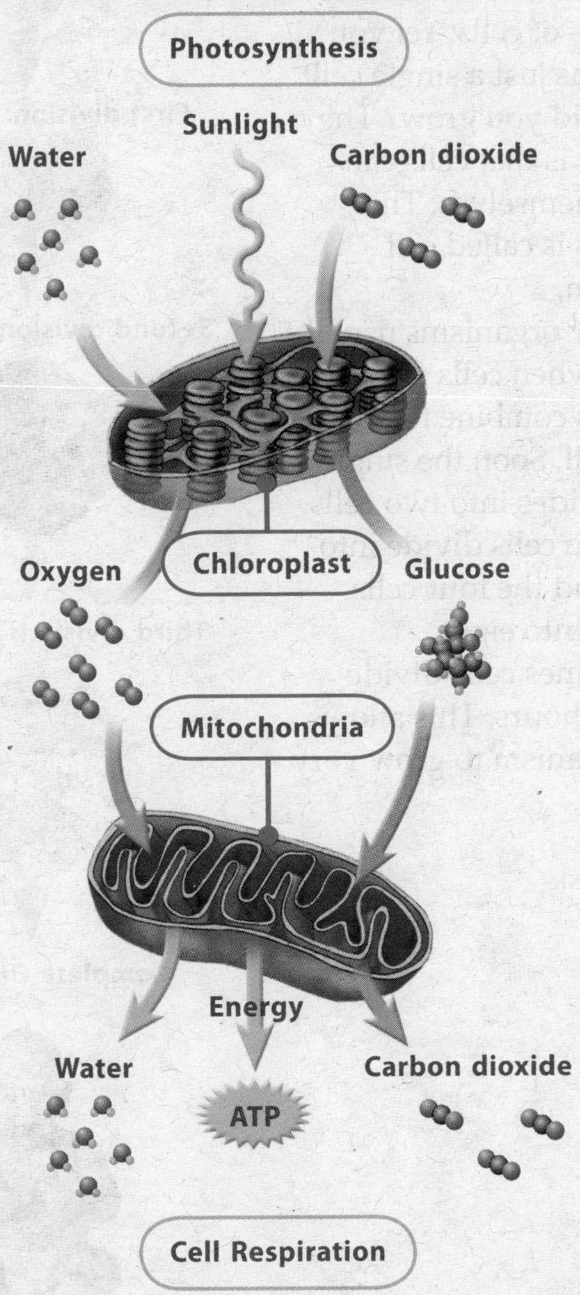

Photosynthesis

Sunlight

Water

Carbon dioxide

Chloroplast

Oxygen

Glucose

Mitochondria

Energy

Water

Carbon dioxide

ATP

Cell Respiration

15. Label each cell part. Tell what the cell part does.

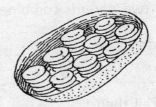

a. _____

_____

b. _____

_____

16. Look at the diagrams on this page. Circle the molecule of energy released during cell respiration. Write the name of this molecule on the line below.

_____

17. Sequence the steps that an organism goes through as it grows.

> **a.** Cells from two parents combine to form a
>
> _____.

⬇

> **b.** This new cell then _____ and forms
>
> _____.

⬇

> **c.** The new cells continue to _____ and
>
> _____.

Cell Division

Your body is made of trillions of cells. Yet you began as just a single cell! How did you grow? The answer is that cells can copy themselves. This process is called cell division.

New organisms usually begin when cells from two parents combine to form a new cell. Soon the single cell divides into two cells. The two cells divide into four, and the four cells divide into eight. Sometimes cells divide within hours. This allows the organism to grow very quickly.

Fertilized Egg

First division: Two cells

Second division: Four cells

Third division: Eight cells

Complete Organism

As cells divide, they differentiate. This means they become different from one another. Early on, the cells organize themselves into three groups, called germ layers. One layer will form the skin and nerves. Another layer becomes the lining of the digestive tract. The third layer produces all other body parts.

Bacteria and other single-celled organisms can also copy themselves. This copying results in new individuals. When conditions favor division, a bacterial colony can double very quickly.

Number of Divisions	1	2	3	4	5
Number of Cells	2	4	8	16	32

A fertilized human egg cell needs about 72 hours to divide three times. After a while, these cells will differentiate and divide millions of times to become a complete organism.

DRAW CONCLUSIONS

How do plants make sugars?

Summary   All living things are made of cells. To stay alive and healthy, cells need food, water, and a way to eliminate waste.

What happens as cells differentiate?

_____

_____

_____

▶ **Draw Conclusions**   How do plants make sugars?

```
┌─────────────────────────────────┐
│ Fact                            │
│ Plants use a process called     │
│ photosynthesis to make food.    │
└─────────────────────────────────┘
              ↓
┌─────────────────────────────────┐
│ Fact                            │
│ Plants use the energy of sunlight. │
└─────────────────────────────────┘
              ↓
┌─────────────────────────────────┐
│ Draw Conclusions                │
│ Plants make sugar by _____ │
│                                 │
│ _____ │
└─────────────────────────────────┘
```

Lesson Preview

VOCABULARY

circulatory system Organ system that carries oxygen to the body and removes carbon dioxide and other wastes. *(noun)*

hormone The chemical message that travels through the blood and carries special information for certain cells. *(noun)*

musculoskeletal system Organ system that supports all parts of your body and allows you to move different parts of your body. *(noun)*

nervous system The organ system—made up of the brain and other nerves—that controls movement and other organ systems. *(noun)*

organ Two or more types of tissue that work together to perform a function. *(noun)*

tissue Group of cells with a common structure and function. *(noun)*

S5L3c. Explain how cells in multi-celled organisms are similar and different in structure and function to single-celled organisms.

2 How Are Cells Specialized?

Complex organisms have many types of cells. Each cell has special structures that allow it to carry out specific tasks.

Different Cells for Different Jobs

Organisms that have many cells have specialized cells that work together. A group of cells that has a common structure and function is called a **tissue**. Plants and animals have tissues that perform specific jobs.

Most complex organisms have a variety of tissues. Epithelial (ehp uh THEE lee uhl) tissues are sheets of cells that cover surfaces. They also line certain body cavities and blood vessels. Epithelial tissues are usually smooth.

Connective tissue joins other tissues together. It also stores fat and makes blood cells. Connective tissue is made of specialized cells and fibers that stick to living cells. Bone, blood, and cartilage are types of connective tissue. Cartilage is the hard material inside your nose and outer ears.

Epidermis

Dermis

Different layers make up your skin. The skin is your body's largest organ.

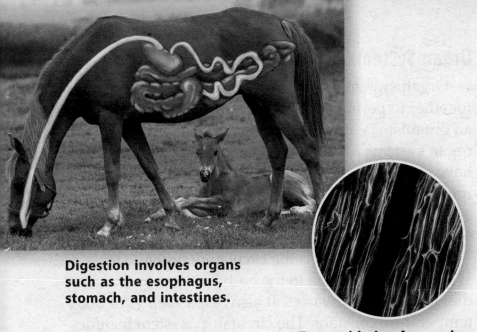

Digestion involves organs such as the esophagus, stomach, and intestines.

Even a blade of grass has several types of tissue.

Most animals use muscle tissues to move. Many muscles work together to move your body. Electrical impulses constantly run through your body and make muscles work. These impulses are produced in nervous tissue. They also move through nervous tissue. Some nervous tissue sends signals. Other nervous tissues protect nerves and provide them with nutrients.

Activities like eating, walking, and running are complex body functions. Body functions are performed by special structures called organs.

An **organ** is made up of several tissue types. These tissues work together to perform one or more functions. Some human organs are the brain, heart, and kidneys. Kidneys are organs that perform more than one function. They remove waste from the body and also help control blood pressure.

1. List four kinds of tissues, and tell what each does.

   a. _____
   _____

   b. _____
   _____

   c. _____
   _____

   d. _____
   _____

2. Explain the relationship among cells, tissues, and organs.

   _____
   _____
   _____

3. List the organs in each system.

a. Circulatory system:

_____

b. Musculoskeletal system:

_____

c. Nervous system:

_____

I Wonder . . . How does your brain help you lift a chair?

_____

_____

_____

_____

Organ Systems

Organ systems are groups of organs that work together to perform complex tasks. The more complex an organism is, the more it needs a greater number of organ systems to carry out life processes. Humans have eleven organ systems. Each plays a particular role in your body. The systems also act on one another. Some organs work for more than one organ system.

One organ system is the **circulatory system**. This system carries oxygen to the body and removes carbon dioxide and other wastes. It also helps keep your body temperature constant. The circulatory system includes your heart, arteries, and veins. At the kidneys, it connects to the urinary system. The urinary system helps control the amount of water and salt in the blood and removes liquid wastes.

The **musculoskeletal system** supports all parts of your body and allows you to move. Bones and muscles make up this system. The bones support the muscles. The muscles contract to make your body parts move.

The brain is the headquarters of the **nervous system**. All your senses feed information into the brain. The brain processes and responds to this information. Often, the brain sends signals down nerves to muscles. The brain also controls the other organ systems.

Your skin is part of an organ system. The inside and outside layers of skin cells protect you from injury and keep in moisture. Four organ systems help your body fight infection and allow you to breathe, eat, and reproduce. Another system produces hormones that control many body functions.

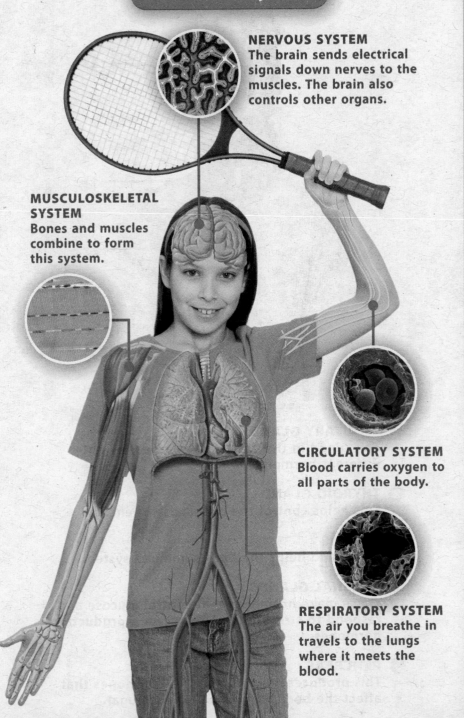

Four Human Systems

NERVOUS SYSTEM
The brain sends electrical signals down nerves to the muscles. The brain also controls other organs.

MUSCULOSKELETAL SYSTEM
Bones and muscles combine to form this system.

CIRCULATORY SYSTEM
Blood carries oxygen to all parts of the body.

RESPIRATORY SYSTEM
The air you breathe in travels to the lungs where it meets the blood.

4. Complete the chart. Tell what each system does.

Organ System	Function
Circulatory system	a. _____
Musculoskeletal system	b. _____ _____ _____
Nervous System	c. _____ _____
Respiratory System	d. _____ _____
Urinary system	e. _____ _____ _____

5. What is the endocrine system?

_____

_____

6. Study the diagram on this page. Choose one gland. (Circle) it. Then tell what the gland does.

_____

_____

GPS **CRCT Prep**

(Circle) the correct answer.

7. **What makes a multi-celled organism different from one that is single-celled?**

A. Only multi-celled organisms have cells that work together to form specific functions.

B. Only multi-celled organisms make energy from sugars.

C. Only multi-celled organisms have organelles.

D. Only multi-celled organisms have cells that divide.

S5L3c

214

Glands and What They Do

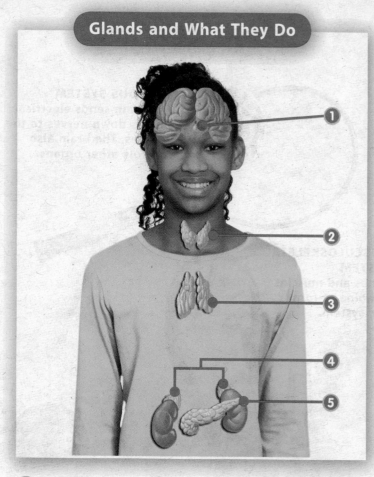

1 PITUITARY GLAND
This gland in the brain makes at least eight different hormones.

2 THYROID GLAND
This helps control the body's use of energy.

3 THYMUS
This gland helps the body's immune system.

4 ADRENAL GLANDS
These make hormones that control glucose and respond to stress. They also act on reproductive hormones.

5 PANCREAS
This produces insulin and other hormones that affect the body's amount of blood sugar.

Endocrine System

Your body's endocrine (EHN duh krihn) system works like a chemical messenger system. The glands of the endocrine system act as communication centers. Endocrine glands are a specialized group of cells that make and send out hormones. A **hormone** acts as a message. It travels through the blood and is picked up only by certain cells.

Humans use about 50 different hormones. Some help to control growth and energy use. Others control blood sugar, minerals, and other chemicals. Some hormones cause specific changes in the body. For example, growth hormones cause dramatic changes in muscles and bones as you grow up. Growth hormones also influence when your growth will stop.

Humans have eleven organ systems. These organ systems work together every day.

MAIN IDEA AND DETAILS

What does the circulatory system do for your body?

Summary Complex organisms have many types of cells. Each cell has special structures that allow it to carry out specific tasks.

What system carries hormones made in the endocrine system throughout the body?

_____

 Main Idea and Details What does the circulatory system do for your body?

> **Main Idea**
>
> The circulatory system is an organ system made up of the heart, arteries, and veins.

Detail	Detail
It carries _____ and _____ throughout the body.	It helps to keep _____ _____ constant.

VOCABULARY

immune system An organ system that fights disease and foreign agents. *(noun)*

infectious disease A disease caused by organisms or viruses. *(noun)*

noninfectious disease A disease caused by malfunction of an organ system. *(noun)*

VOCABULARY SKILL: Prefixes

Read the definition of the term *noninfectious disease*. The prefix *non-* means "not." Use this information to rewrite the definition of noninfectious disease.

_____

_____

3 How Does Disease Affect Cells?

Disease affects the structure and function of cells. The body has developed defenses and weapons against many diseases. Medicines help fight disease, too.

Causes of Diseases

Many things can cause sickness or disease. Some diseases happen when harmful organisms or viruses enter the body. Other diseases happen when body systems do not work correctly.

An **infectious disease** is caused by harmful organisms or viruses. Bacteria and some kinds of fungi can cause infectious disease. Certain kinds of worms can get stuck in the intestines or muscles and cause serious diseases.

Organisms carried by mosquitoes can cause infectious disease. Food and water can also carry organisms that cause disease. Contagious diseases can spread easily from person to person. Diseases that do not spread between people are not contagious.

Things that cause infectious disease can multiply quickly after a natural disaster like the tsunami of December 2004.

GPS **S5L4b.** Identify harmful microorganisms and explain why they are harmful.

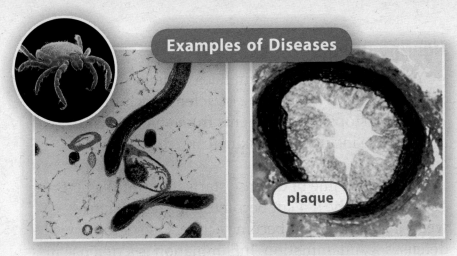

Examples of Diseases

plaque

LYME DISEASE
Ticks carry the spirochete bacteria that cause this disease. The ticks are about the size of a pinhead.

ARTERIOSCLEROSIS
This artery is almost entirely blocked by plaque, fatty substances that stick to the artery wall. Eating a healthy diet can help keep arteries clear of plaque.

Viruses are common causes of infectious disease. Viruses are not made of cells, so they are not organisms, but viruses can take over a normal cell and cause the cell to make more viruses. Many diseases caused by viruses are mild. Others are more dangerous and even deadly.

A **noninfectious disease** occurs when a body system does not work correctly. Such a disease cannot spread from person to person. Sometimes the disease is caused by a condition that is inherited from your family. Other times a disease appears as a person's body ages.

Healthy lifestyles and habits can help prevent many of these later-in-life diseases. Poor nutrition causes many noninfectious diseases. People who do not receive the proper vitamins in their food can suffer a variety of illnesses or damaged organs.

1. Compare and contrast infectious and non-infectious diseases.

Infectious diseases

Caused by

_____

_____

or _____.

_____

spread from

person to

person.

Both affect the structure and function of cells.

Noninfectious diseases

Caused by

_____

_____.

_____

spread from

person to

person.

I Wonder . . . Is arteriosclerosis contagious?

_____

_____

_____

2. List five natural parts of the body that are barriers against invasion by harmful organisms.

a. _____

b. _____

c. _____

d. _____

e. _____

3. What behavior helps keep your body well?

_____

4. Describe the body's second line of defense.

_____

_____

Fighting Disease

Your body has three main lines of defense against disease agents. The first line of defense includes ways your body stops disease agents from entering your body. These include your skin, tears, saliva, earwax, and mucus.

The second line of defense starts if harmful agents enter your body. If a cut becomes infected, defense weapons in the blood become active. One of these defenses is inflammation. Inflammation is a defense in which your blood reacts to fight infection. Your body is starting the healing process.

The second line of defense can include the production of special cells called phagocytes (FAG uh syts). These cells surround and consume harmful disease agents that invade your body. Phagocytes are one type of white blood cell.

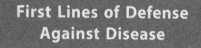

First Lines of Defense Against Disease

Mucus in your nose traps harmful organisms and keeps them from going farther into your body.

Saliva in your mouth has strong chemicals that can kill many types of bacteria.

Acids in your stomach can kill bacteria and other harmful organisms.

Washing your skin helps remove harmful bacteria and other infectious agents, and keeps you from passing them on to others.

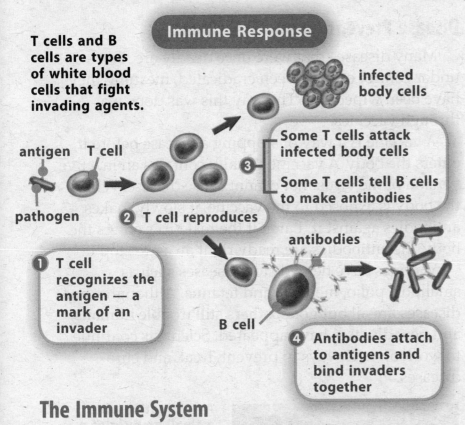

T cells and B cells are types of white blood cells that fight invading agents.

Immune Response

antigen   T cell

pathogen

infected body cells

3 Some T cells attack infected body cells

Some T cells tell B cells to make antibodies

2 T cell reproduces

1 T cell recognizes the antigen — a mark of an invader

antibodies

B cell

4 Antibodies attach to antigens and bind invaders together

The Immune System

The **immune system** is your body's third line of defense. This system fights harmful agents of disease. It uses special cells that recognize these invaders.

Many cells produced by the immune system attack disease agents and destroy them. Certain types of white blood cells produce special proteins called antibodies that fight invading agents.

After the invading cells are destroyed, the body begins to recover from sickness. Some of the immune system's special white blood cells remain in the body. If the same invaders attack the body again, these cells can immediately produce the needed antibodies. The body is then immune to, or protected from, that particular illness.

5. What is the body's third line of defense?

_____

6. Fill in the blanks to explain the steps of the immune response.

a. A disease-causing agent called a
    _____ invades the body.

b. A _____ recognizes the antigen of
    the _____ .

c. The T cell _____ .

d. Some T cells attack _____ .
    Others tell _____ to make antibodies.

e. Antibodies attach to _____
    and bind _____ together.

Summary Disease affects the structure and function of cells. The body has developed defenses and weapons against many diseases. Medicines help fight disease, too. What does it mean when a disease has been eradicated?

_____

_____

▶ **Cause and Effect** How does a vaccine help your body fight viral infection?

Cause		Effect
You receive a vaccine for an infectious disease caused by a virus.	→	_____ _____ _____

Disease Prevention and Treatment

Many diseases that were once deadly are now under control or have been eradicated, meaning they have been wiped out. The way this was done was through vaccines.

A vaccine is a way of stopping a disease before it enters the body. A vaccine usually contains an inactive version of the virus that cannot cause disease. When the body is exposed to the vaccine, it slowly makes antibodies against it. Later, if the real virus enters the body, the antibodies are ready right away to stop it.

Vaccines have helped stop diseases such as smallpox, polio, measles, and tetanus. Although some diseases are all but gone, others still trouble humans, and new diseases have appeared. Scientists continue to work on new ways to prevent, treat, and cure diseases.

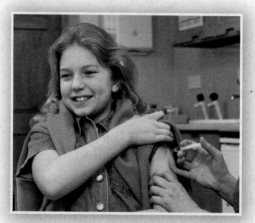

A vaccination puts a small amount of a live or dead virus into the body. The vaccine causes the immune system to develop antibodies.

CAUSE AND EFFECT

How does a vaccine help your body fight viral infection?

chloroplast (KLAWR uh plast), an organelle that makes food from sunlight, water, and carbon dioxide

circulatory system (SUR kyuh luh tawr ee SIHS tuhm), organ system that carries oxygen to the body and removes carbon dioxide and other wastes

cytoplasm (SY tuh plaz uhm), the gel-like material that surrounds the internal parts of the cell

diffusion (dih FYOO zhuhn), process that spreads substances through a gas or liquid from higher to lower concentration

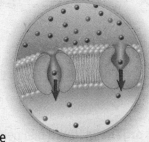

hormone (HAWR mohn), the chemical message that travels through the blood and carries special information for certain cells

immune system (ih MYOON SIHS tuhm), an organ system that fights disease and foreign agents

infectious disease (ihn FEHK shuhs dih ZEEZ), a disease caused by organisms or viruses

What do the circulatory system and the immune system have in common?

_____

_____

_____

221

Visit www.eduplace.com/gascp to play word games and puzzles.

Glossary

musculoskeletal system (muhs kyuh loh SKEHL ih tuhl SIHS tuhm), organ system that supports all parts of your body and allows you to move different parts of your body

nervous system (NUR vuhs SIHS tuhm), the organ system—made up of the brain and other nerves—that controls movement and other organ systems

noninfectious disease (nahn ihn FEHK shuhs dih ZEEZ), a disease caused by malfunction of an organ system

nucleus (NOO klee uhs), a part of a cell that directs all cell activities and carries information for cell reproduction

organelle (AWR guh nehl), a structure that has a specific task within the cell

organ (AWR guhn), two or more types of tissue that work together to perform a function

osmosis (ahz MOH sihs), a type of diffusion that allows water to pass but not the solutes in the water

tissue (TIHSH oo), group of cells with a common structure and function

Think About What You Have Read

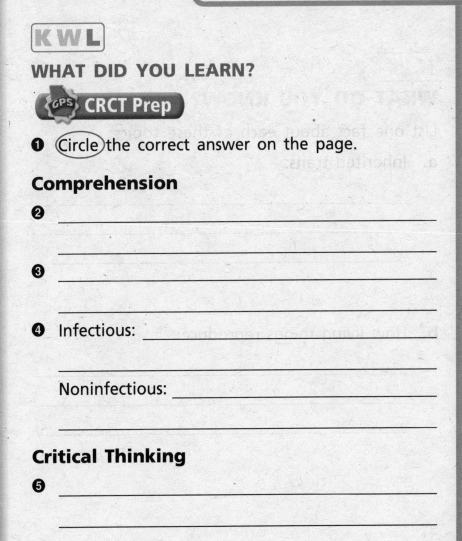

CRCT Prep

❶ Special proteins produced by the body to fight viruses are called

   A. antibodies.

   B. spirochetes.

   C. bacteria.

   D. medicine.

S5L4b

Comprehension

❷ What do cells need to stay alive?

❸ What are specialized cells?

❹ What causes infectious and noninfectious diseases?

Critical Thinking

❺ You notice that you get more colds when you don't wash your hands very often. What conclusion can you draw from this?

KWL

WHAT DID YOU LEARN?

CRCT Prep

❶ (Circle) the correct answer on the page.

Comprehension

❷ _____

   _____

❸ _____

   _____

❹ Infectious: _____

   _____

   Noninfectious: _____

   _____

Critical Thinking

❺ _____

   _____

WHAT DO YOU KNOW?

List one fact about each of these topics:

a. Inherited traits:

_____

_____

_____

b. How living things reproduce:

_____

_____

_____

Traits of Living Things

Contents

WHAT DO YOU WANT TO KNOW?

Skim the pictures and headings in this chapter. List one thing you want to find out about each of these topics:

a. Mutations:

_____

_____

_____

b. Selective breeding:

_____

_____

_____

VOCABULARY

acquired trait Characteristic that an organism develops after it is born. *(noun)*

chromosomes Short, thick coils of DNA. *(noun)*

DNA Molecule found in the nucleus of a cell and shaped like a double helix; associated with the transfer of genetic information. *(noun)*

gene Short segment of DNA that determines an organism's inherited traits. *(noun)*

heredity Genetic transfer of characteristics from parent to offspring. *(noun)*

mutation Change in the genes of an organism. *(noun)*

nucleotide Basic structural unit of DNA. *(noun)*

VOCABULARY SKILL: Related Words

Look at the pictures on these two pages. Identify which are showing acquired traits and which are showing inherited traits.

_____

_____

_____

GPS **S5L2a.** Compare and contrast the characteristics of learned behaviors and of inherited traits.

1 How Are Traits Inherited?

Living things get, or inherit, traits such as eye color or face shape from their parents. They get other traits from their environment.

Traits of Organisms

Do you look like anyone in your family? People often look like their parents and grandparents because of heredity. **Heredity** is the process through which traits are passed from parents to their offspring.

Human traits that are passed by heredity are called inherited traits. Face shape, hair color, and blood type are inherited traits. In animals, fur color and ear shape are inherited traits. The colors of a flower or the shape of a fruit are inherited traits in plants. An inherited trait can also be a behavior, such as how a spider spins a web.

Not all traits are passed through heredity. Some traits are picked up along the way, or acquired. An **acquired trait** is a trait an organism develops after it is born. Some acquired traits come from the environment, and some are learned.

Inherited traits are passed from parents to children through cell structures called chromosomes.

Environmental Traits

Organisms can acquire traits from their environments. A flamingo is pink because it eats pink food.

Learned Traits

Organisms can acquire traits by learning and remembering skills and information.

Acquired Traits

Bright pink flamingos have a trait that most other long-legged water birds do not have—their color! The color comes from pigments in shrimp and algae that flamingos eat.

The pink color of flamingos is an acquired trait. This trait comes from something in the flamingos' environment. Organisms can acquire traits from food, soil, water, and other parts of their environment.

Some acquired traits are learned. You were not born knowing how to ride a bicycle or skateboard. You learned how to ride. All types of animals learn how to do things. Dogs can learn to sit, and lions can learn to hunt. These kinds of acquired traits are called learned traits.

Sometimes people change traits on purpose. These are called manipulated traits. Gardeners mix plants with good traits to produce plants with certain shapes and sizes.

1. Compare and contrast inherited and acquired traits.

Inherited traits

Traits are passed from _____ to _____.

Two examples are _____ and _____.

A quality that makes two organisms of the same kind different from one another

Acquired traits

Traits come from the _____ or are _____.

Two examples are _____ _____ and _____ _____.

227

Circle the correct answer.

2. Information about inherited traits is
   stored in

   A. ATP.

   B. DNA.

   C. chloroplasts.

   D. cytoplasm.

3. Read about how DNA changes as a cell gets
   ready to divide. Circle the chromosome in the
   diagram.

Chromosomes and Genes

How does an organism inherit certain traits? Information about traits is stored in the cell nucleus in a molecule called **DNA**. A DNA molecule is made of two, long pieces called strands that are side by side. The strands wind around each other like edges of a twisted ladder.

Molecules of DNA are passed from a parent to a child during reproduction. Remember that organisms make offspring during a process called reproduction. For DNA to pass from parents to offspring, a copy of the DNA molecules must be made.

As a cell gets ready to divide, the strands of DNA wind up tightly. They form shorter, thicker strands of DNA. This DNA forms rod-shaped structures called **chromosomes**. In a dividing cell, each chromosome is made of two halves that are exactly the same. These halves are called chromatids.

Cells and DNA

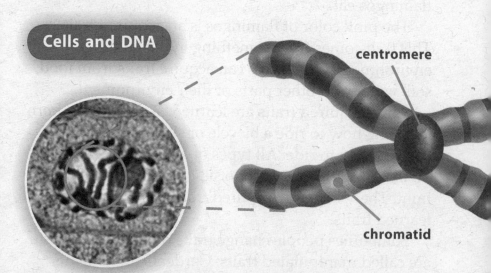

centromere

chromatid

CELL Just before a cell divides, its DNA winds tightly into rod-shaped chromosomes.

Most organisms have cells with pairs of chromosomes. The chromosomes in each pair are alike, but not exactly the same. Different living things have different numbers of chromosomes per cell. Human cells have 46 chromosomes. Dog cells have 78.

In every plant and animal, one kind of cell is made with only half the chromosomes of other cells. These special cells are used for reproduction. They are called gametes, or egg and sperm cells. Human gametes have 23 chromosomes.

When two gametes join, their chromosomes become part of the nucleus of a cell of a new person. The new cell now has a full set of 46 chromosomes.

There are many more traits than chromosomes because the information in one chromosome can affect many traits. Each trait of an organism is decided by a short piece of DNA called a **gene**. One chromosome can have hundreds of genes on it.

CHROMOSOME A chromosome is made of two strands, or chromatids, that are exactly the same. The chromatids meet at the centromere. The DNA is organized into units called genes.

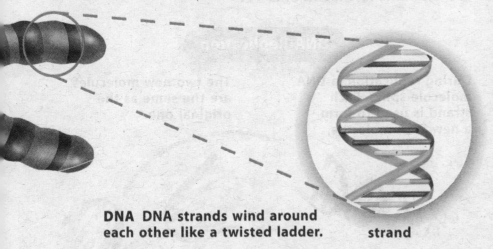

DNA DNA strands wind around each other like a twisted ladder.   strand

4. Tell how many chromosomes are in each type of human cell.

   a. body cells: _____

   b. gametes: _____

I Wonder . . . If gametes have only 23 chromosomes, how do offspring get the full 46 chromosomes that are in each cell?

_____

_____

_____

_____

5. Tell how genes and chromosomes are related.

_____

_____

_____

6. The diagram below shows a molecule of _____.

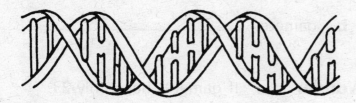

a. In the diagram above (circle) a pair of nitrogen bases.

b. Put an X on an area made of phosphate and sugars.

7. What process is beginning in the molecule above? How do you know?

_____

_____

The Structure of DNA

DNA is made of units called **nucleotides**. Each nucleotide is made up of a phosphate, a sugar, and a nitrogen base. There are four different nitrogen bases.

Remember that a molecule of DNA looks like a ladder. The phosphates and sugars make up the sides of the ladder. Pairs of nitrogen bases make up the steps.

An organism's genes are decided by the order of the nitrogen bases in its DNA. The bases can be arranged in many different ways. This makes many different genes possible.

DNA Replication

Before a cell divides, a copy of its DNA is made through a process called DNA replication. To begin, the strands of the DNA molecule break apart along their nitrogen bases. This forms two strands of DNA.

Next, floating nitrogen bases stick to the bases of the DNA strands. This forms a new strand on each of the old strands, making two new DNA molecules that are the same as the old one.

DNA Replication

During replication, a DNA molecule splits. Each strand is used to form a new DNA molecule.

The two new molecules are the same as the original one.

Making Proteins

DNA controls the making, or production, of substances called proteins. Proteins control most of the life processes in cells. They also help build cells and keep them healthy. Proteins also cause certain traits to appear in an organism.

Proteins are made up of smaller units called amino acids. There are 20 different amino acids that can be combined in different ways.

Remember that proteins are formed on cell organelles called ribosomes. With the help of other molecules, DNA controls the way the amino acids are set up to make these proteins. This means that DNA really controls everything a cell does!

In this boy's DNA is the gene for one of his traits—red hair.

8. List three functions of proteins in the body.

a. _____

b. _____

c. _____

9. Fill in the blanks to summarize how proteins are made.

a. Proteins are made up of smaller units called _____.

b. There are _____ different kinds of these units.

c. The molecule that controls the way the amino acids are set up to make proteins is _____.

d. In this way, _____ controls everything a cell does.

10. Look at the diagram below. What process is occurring in this section of DNA? How do you know?

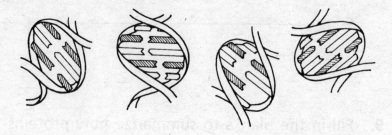

_____

_____

I Wonder . . . Are mutations always harmful? Explain your answer.

_____

_____

_____

_____

_____

Mutations

Sometimes, a mistake happens during DNA replication. This kind of change is called a **mutation**.

A mutation may cause a change in the proteins that are made in a cell. Many mutations are harmful because they make it harder for an organism to stay alive. In rare cases, mutations are helpful because they cause new, welcomed traits.

Some mutations are not harmful or helpful. They do not harm an organism or make it hard for it to live.

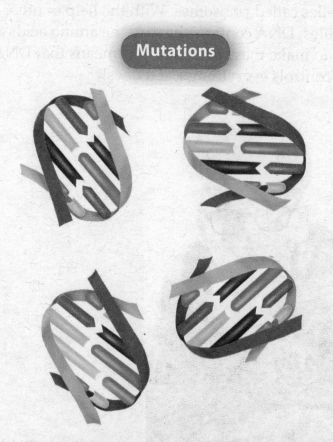

Mutations

Look for differences between the molecules. These differences are called mutations.

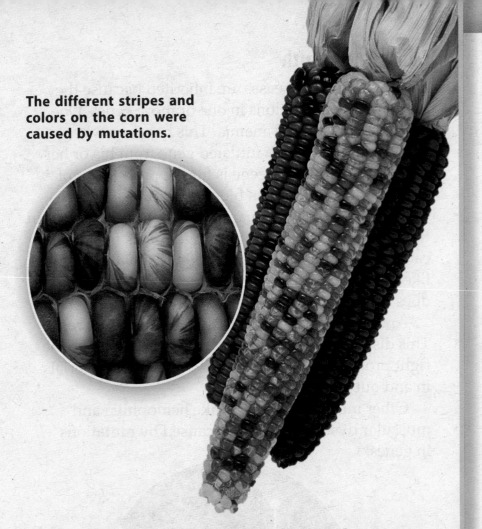

The different stripes and colors on the corn were caused by mutations.

11. Define mutagen.

_____

_____

12. List two mutagens.

a. _____

b. _____

13. How do you know if a mutation can be inherited by offspring?

_____

_____

Many mutations happen for no reason at all. Other mutations are caused by things in the environment, called mutagens. Ultraviolet radiation from the Sun, and certain chemicals, like the ones farmers use to kill pests (pesticides), can be mutagens.

Can a mutation be passed from a parent to its offspring? It depends on the cell that has the mutation. If the mutation affects a gamete—a sperm cell or egg cell—the mutation may be passed from the parent to the offspring. If the mutation affects a body cell only, it is not passed from the parent to the offspring.

14. List four inherited diseases caused by mutations in genes.

a. _____

b. _____

c. _____

d. _____

15. Describe how down syndrome occurs.

_____

_____

_____

Genes and Health

Some human diseases are inherited because they are caused by mutations in one or more genes. One example is sickle cell anemia. This happens when a person has inherited a mutated gene from his or her parents. The mutated gene is for the production of hemoglobin, a protein in blood that carries oxygen.

With sickle cell anemia, one of the nitrogen bases in the gene for hemoglobin is changed. This mistake causes protein to make red blood cells that are shaped like the letter C, instead of being round. This C-shape does not let the cells work correctly.

Another inherited disease is called cystic fibrosis. This disease is caused by genes that do not make the right proteins to control the flow of certain materials in and out of cells.

Other inherited diseases, like hemophilia and muscular dystrophy, are also caused by mutations in genes.

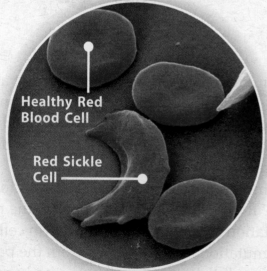

Healthy Red Blood Cell

Red Sickle Cell

Sickle cell anemia makes blood cells with a C shape. Sickle cells get in the way of other blood cells.

Other genetic disorders, or problems with genes, occur when chromosomes do not split apart in the right way during reproduction.

Remember that chromosomes are copied before a cell divides. The copies split apart, and one copy goes to each new cell. Down syndrome is a genetic disorder that occurs when a certain pair of chromosomes does not split apart correctly. The extra chromosome causes physical and mental problems.

Inherited Diseases

Disorder	Description
Cystic Fibrosis	Makes body mucus extra thick and sticky. This makes it hard for a person to breathe and digest food.
Hemophilia	Makes it hard for a person to stop bleeding, because the blood does not produce clotting factors.
Muscular Dystrophy	Prevents the body from making protein for muscle cells, which makes a person's muscles weak.
Sickle Cell Anemia	Makes red blood cells that are shaped like the letter C. Sickle cells block other cells in the blood, and do not carry as much oxygen as healthy red blood cells.

SEQUENCE

Why do body cells have twice as many chromosomes as gametes?

Summary   Living things inherit many traits from their parents. They acquire others from their environment.

What information would a scientist need to determine whether a trait was hereditary or acquired?

_____

_____

▶ **Sequence**   Why do body cells have twice as many chromosomes as gametes?

The parent organisms produce gametes that have half the number of chromosomes.

↓

The gametes _____ to form _____ that have _____ the number of chromosomes that each gamete has.

235

Lesson Preview

VOCABULARY

adaptation A trait or characteristic that helps an organism survive in its environment. *(noun)*

asexual reproduction The production of offspring from only one parent. *(noun)*

dominant Describes a trait that is expressed when an organism receives genes for two different forms of a trait. *(adjective)*

hybrid An organism that has two different genes for the same trait. *(noun)*

recessive Describes a trait that is not expressed when an organism receives genes for two different forms of a trait. *(adjective)*

selective breeding The practice of breeding plants and animals for desirable traits. *(noun)*

sexual reproduction The production of offspring by the union of male and female gametes. *(noun)*

VOCABULARY SKILL: Prefixes

The prefix *a-* means "not." Use this information to write your own definition of *asexual reproduction.*

_____

_____

_____

2 Why Are Some Traits Very Common?

Over many years of reproduction, groups of animals develop traits that help them stay alive.

Asexual Reproduction

Some organisms need only one parent to reproduce. In **asexual reproduction**, offspring are produced from one parent. Bacteria and many protists usually reproduce asexually.

When an organism reproduces asexually, a copy of DNA is passed from the parent to the offspring. Each time the offspring reproduces, it has the same DNA as the very first parent. Mutations are the only way new traits form during asexual reproduction.

Plants have several different asexual structures. Some plants grow plantlets, or baby plants. Plantlets can break off or be cut away from the parent plant. Other plants can grow from root cuttings or pieces of stem.

Plantlets can be cut away from the parent plant. Each plantlet can become a separate plant.

Plantlet

New Roots

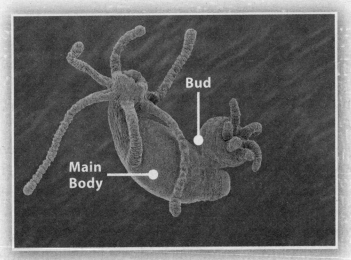

Bud

Main Body

BUDDING Hydra are animals that can reproduce asexually by budding. They can also reproduce sexually using male and female gametes.

In the simplest organisms, such as bacteria, most or all reproduction is asexual. Other organisms use asexual reproduction some of the time. For example, yeast can switch between asexual reproduction and sexual reproduction.

A yeast makes buds asexually. The bud breaks off from the yeast cell and begins to grow. Other times, the yeast makes male and female gametes. These cells can join to make a new yeast cell through sexual reproduction.

Another asexual process in some animals is regeneration. Through regeneration, flatworms called *planaria* can reproduce. If a planaria is cut in half, each half will grow to produce two whole worms.

Cells divide during asexual reproduction and regeneration. In both processes, the new cells have the same DNA as the original cells. Replicating and passing DNA from parent to offspring helps keep traits the same.

1. Tell how each of these types of organisms reproduces asexually.

   a. plants: _____

   b. yeast: _____

   c. flatworms: _____

I Wonder . . . Can a species of organism that reproduces by asexual reproduction develop new traits over time?

_____

_____

_____

_____

237

2. Compare and contrast sexual and asexual reproduction.

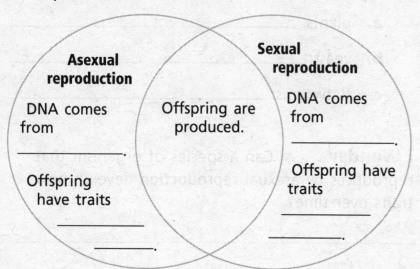

Asexual reproduction

DNA comes from

_____.

Offspring have traits

_____

Offspring are produced.

Sexual reproduction

DNA comes from

_____.

Offspring have traits

_____

_____.

Sexual Reproduction

Sexual reproduction happens when a female gamete joins with a male gamete to form a new organism. Many plants and animals use sexual reproduction.

A flowering plant has male and female reproductive parts in its flowers. Pollination happens when pollen moves from the male part, a stamen, to the female part, a pistil. A sperm cell that is released by the pollen then fertilizes an egg cell.

You have learned that gametes contain half the number of chromosomes as body cells. When a sperm cell joins an egg cell, the chromosomes become part of the same cell. This is a new cell with a complete set of chromosomes.

In this way, the offspring gets one chromosome in each pair from each of its parents. Each chromosome has genes that set the traits of the offspring. The offspring gets two genes for each of its traits.

Animals like bees and birds help pollination occur by moving pollen from one flower to another.

Different genes may hold information for different forms of the same trait. Think about a bee that carries pollen from a red flower to a yellow flower. The offspring may get a gene for red flower color and a gene for yellow flower color. Red and yellow are two forms of the same trait—flower color.

Some forms of a trait are stronger, and other forms of a trait are weaker. If an offspring gets genes for two different forms of a trait, the trait of the stronger, or **dominant** gene shows in the offspring. The trait of the weaker, or **recessive** gene does not show.

If a bee carries pollen from this pink rose to a white rose, what color will the offspring be? If the gene for pink petals is dominant, the offspring will be a pink flower.

Circle the correct answer.

3. The stronger gene for a given trait is called the _____ gene.

   A. dominant

   B. recessive

   C. DNA

   D. chromosomic

S5L2b

4. Fill in the blanks to describe the steps in pollination.

a. Pollen contains the _____ sex cells.

⬇

b. Pollen is moved from _____ to _____.

⬇

c. The _____ is deep inside the flower. The pollen is brushed onto the female part of the flower.

⬇

d. The _____ contains DNA from both parents.

⬇

e. _____ develop from the fertilized eggs. Their DNA comes from both parents.

Pretend that red flowers are dominant for a certain plant. An offspring plant that gets a gene for red flowers from each of its parents will have red flowers. An offspring plant that gets one gene for red flowers and one gene for yellow flowers from its parents will also have red flowers. That is because the dominant trait (red flowers) will show instead of the recessive trait (yellow flowers). Only offspring that gets a gene for yellow flowers from both parents will have yellow flowers.

An organism that has two of the same genes for a trait is called a purebred. A purebred organism can have two dominant genes or two recessive genes.

① **POLLEN** Pollen contains male sex cells that have the male genes.

② **POLLINATION** A bee or other pollinator moves male genes in pollen from flower to flower.

③ **EGG** The egg is deep inside the flower. The bee brushes pollen onto the female parts as it looks for nectar to eat.

An organism that has two different genes for the same trait is called a **hybrid**. The offspring of hybrids may show traits that neither of its parents has. Think about the red and yellow flowers again. If a bee carries pollen from a red flower to a red flower, you might think that all of the offspring would have red flowers, if red flowers are dominant.

But, if the parents are hybrids, they each could carry a gene for yellow flowers—even if you don't see it. If an offspring happens to get the gene for yellow flowers from both parents, it will show the recessive trait of yellow flowers.

④ The fertilized egg contains DNA from both parents.

⑤ Seeds contain the embryos, or first cells, of the next plants. Their DNA comes from both parents.

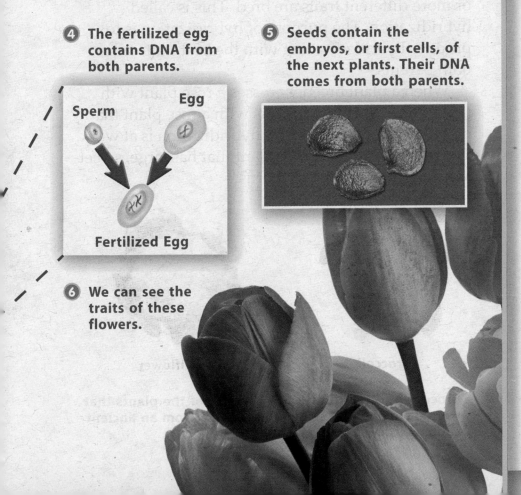

Sperm
Egg

Fertilized Egg

⑥ We can see the traits of these flowers.

5. Define *hybrid*.

_____

_____

I Wonder . . . Why might the traits of offspring of hybrids be difficult to predict?

_____

_____

_____

_____

6. Why do people selectively breed plants and animals?

_____

_____

7. List two kinds of selective breeding and tell what each is.

a.

_____

_____

b.

_____

_____

Selective Breeding

For thousands of years, people have noticed good traits in plants and animals. They have worked to increase these traits. Long before scientists knew about chromosomes and genes, farmers were breeding, or encouraging reproduction between, plants and animals to get offspring with useful traits.

Breeding plants and animals for useful traits is called **selective breeding**. Through selective breeding, people try to plan the genes in offspring without actually changing the genes in any way.

In one form of selective breeding, parents with two or more different traits are bred. This is called hybridization. The purpose of hybridization is to produce hybrid offspring with the best traits from both parents.

When a plant breeder crosses a rose plant with large, sweet-smelling flowers with a rose plant that does not have sharp thorns, hybridization is at work. The result might be a rose plant that has large, sweet-smelling flowers and no thorns.

broccoli   **cauliflower**

Broccoli and cauliflower are just two of the plants that were developed by selective breeding from an ancient cabbage plant.

In another type of selective breeding, plants and animals with the same or similar traits are combined. This produces offspring with traits that will be very similar to the traits of their parents. This method is called inbreeding. Horses and dogs are often bred in this way.

One problem with inbreeding is that offspring do not inherit new groups of genes from their parents. This means that the genes of the offspring are very similar. Changes in environment, like harsh weather or diseases, can harm organisms that are similar. Groups of organisms with different genes might survive these changes in environment better than organisms with genes that are alike.

Today, farmers and ranchers have other ways to make plants and animals better. Chemicals can make hens lay more eggs and make cows produce more milk. Computers can help breeders understand the good and bad results of selective breeding.

This is a dairy cow. It is bred to produce milk. Beef cows are bred to produce beef.

8. Why can inbreeding affect the long-term survival of organisms?

_____

_____

_____

I Wonder . . . Why might farmers use methods other than selective breeding to improve crops and animals?

_____

_____

_____

_____

_____

9. Factors that help organisms eat, reproduce, and stay safe in their environments are called

_____.

10. Tell how each bird's beak shape is adapted to help it find food.

pelican:

_____

_____

hummingbird:

_____

_____

parrot:

_____

_____

Adaptations

In nature, useful traits are not always traits that people would prefer. They are usually the traits that help an organism survive. Any trait that helps a living thing survive in its environment is called an **adaptation**. Adaptations help organisms eat, reproduce, and stay safe in their environments.

For example, beak shape is an adaptation that helps birds find food. The shape of a pelican's beak is an adaptation that helps the bird scoop up fish from the water. A hummingbird's long, thin beak is an adaptation that helps it reach nectar that is deep inside flowers. A parrot's beak is short and thick, which helps it crack and open seeds.

Spines or stingers keep enemies, or predators, away or hurt them if they come too close. Thorns, spines, or tough leaves are adaptations that protect plants from being eaten.

A long, deep beak helps a pelican scoop up fish.

CAMOUFLAGE
The walking stick is an insect that looks like a stick or twig. It can hide easily in a tree.

MIMICRY
The king snake stays safe because it looks like a dangerous coral snake.

Camouflage Many adaptations protect organisms from predators. Camouflage is when an organism can hide in the environment around it. Organisms with camouflage can hide from predators.

For example, some insects look like the flowers of their favorite plants. It is hard to see the insects when they are on the plants. Bees usually collect honey when there are many shadows. Their black stripes look like shadows.

Mimicry When an organism looks like another organism, we call it mimicry. An organism might look like, or mimic, another organism that is more dangerous to a predator. For example, the king snake is not poisonous, but it mimics the poisonous coral snake so predators will stay away from it.

11. This insect has an adaptation that helps it blend in with its environment. What is this adaptation called?

_____

12. How does mimicry help an organism?

_____

_____

_____

245

Summary Over many generations, species develop traits that help them to survive. How do bright colors help keep some organisms safe from predators?

_____

_____

_____

▶ **Cause and Effect** In sexual reproduction, how many cells join to make a new organism?

Cause		Effect
_____ cells join.	→	A new organism is formed.

Warning Colors Bright colors often mean that an organism is poisonous. The colors warn predators to stay away. Many frogs have brightly colored skin that shows that they are poisonous. A predator that eats one poisonous frog is not likely to eat any others, because it will get sick.

Sometimes two organisms have adaptations that work together. For example, butterflies like plants that have many flowers in large groups. The butterflies can eat the nectar from these flowers without using much energy to fly from flower to flower. The butterflies help the flowers by moving pollen between them.

WARNING COLORS
The red and yellow skin of the poison arrow frog tells predators that it is poisonous.

CAUSE AND EFFECT

In sexual reproduction, how many cells join to make a new organism?

Glossary

acquired trait (uh KWYRD trayt), characteristic that an organism develops after it is born.

adaptation (ad ap TAY shuhn), a trait or characteristic that helps an organism survive in its environment.

asexual reproduction (ay SEHK shoo uhl ree pruh DUHK shuhn), production of offspring from only one parent.

chromosome (KROH muh sohm), short, thick coil of DNA.

DNA molecule found in the nucleus of a cell and shaped like a double helix; associated with the transfer of genetic information.

dominant (DAHM uh nuhnt), describes a trait that is expressed when an organism receives genes for two different forms of a trait.

gene (jeen), short segment of DNA that determines an organism's inherited traits.

Circle the words that are related to the part of the cell responsible for passing on traits. Then tell how the three words are related.

_____

_____

_____

247

Visit www.eduplace.com/gascp to play word games and puzzles.

Glossary

heredity (huh REHD ih tee), genetic transfer of characteristics from parent to offspring.

hybrid (HY brihd), organism that has two different genes for the same trait.

mutation (myoo TAY shuhn), change in the genes of an organism.

nucleotide (NOO klee uh tyd), basic structural unit of DNA.

recessive (rih SEHS ihv), describes a trait that is not expressed when an organism receives genes for two different forms of a trait.

selective breeding (suh LEHK tihv BREE ding), practice of breeding plants and animals for desirable traits.

sexual reproduction (SEHK shoo uhl ree pruh DUHK shuhn), production of offspring by the union of male and female gametes.

Responding

Think About What You Have Read

CRCT Prep

❶ **An adaptation is best described as**

A. a series of learned or acquired traits.

B. the result of experimentation by humans.

C. a trait that is favorable to survival.

D. an attempt to grow stronger than other organisms.

S5L2b

Comprehension

❷ What material carries the information that determines inherited traits?

❸ How do mutations affect an organism? Why can some mutations have no effect?

❹ What process do people use to influence the traits of a plant or animal?

Critical Thinking

❺ List three inherited or acquired traits that help you survive, and explain why each trait helps you.

Chapter Review

KWL

WHAT DID YOU LEARN?

CRCT Prep

❶ Circle the correct answer on the page.

Comprehension

❷ ______________________________

____

❸ ______________________________

____

❹ ______________________________

____

Critical Thinking

❺ ______________________________

____

____

____